ISAAC NEWTON

At the age of twenty-four, Isaac Newton made four discoveries which were to excite the world of science and which have proved to be important in modern mathematics, physics, chemistry and astronomy. He discovered the law of gravitation; proved that the Inverse Square Law accounted for the motion of the moon around the earth; discovered the composition of light and invented the reflecting telescope; and was co-discoverer of a mathematical science called calculus.

ISAAC NEWTON

by *HARRY SOOTIN*

author of MICHAEL FARADAY:

From Errand Boy to Master Physicist

Julian Messner, Inc. *New York*

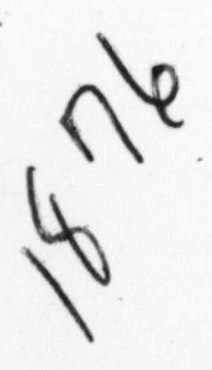

92
new

Published by Julian Messner, Inc.
8 West 40th Street, New York 18
Published simultaneously in Canada
by The Copp Clark Company, Ltd.

Printed in the United States of America

Library of Congress Catalog Card No. 55-9868

Sixth Printing, 1962

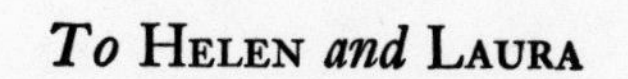

To HELEN *and* LAURA

CONTENTS

ISAAC NEWTON

1

THE RAID

It was well after midnight when a detachment of Cromwell's hard-riding cavalry swooped down on the tiny village of Woolesthorpe in Lincolnshire. The Civil War in England, in 1650, was still being carried on by bands of fanatical Royalists, even though Charles I had been beheaded by the Puritans the year before.

The leader pulled his horse up hard and stopped in front of a two-story stone manor house which in the moonlight looked like a deserted fortress. He dismounted quickly, ran to the low narrow door facing the road and pounded on it with the handle of his sword. There was no response from within. He became impatient and proceeded to hammer out an even louder summons.

"I hear a stirring," he said, turning to his men who were waiting behind him with cocked muskets.

"They'll get away," observed one of the soldiers, "if we tarry here too long."

"Someone is coming now," said the man at the door.

There was a fumbling with the latch and soon the door swung slowly open, revealing a tall white-haired woman whose protective arm was around the shoulders of a wide-eyed, tense boy of about eight.

"Did you see Wentworth's gang go by here?" asked the leader sternly as he eyed the elderly woman with open suspicion.

She shook her head as she tried to control her trembling lips. "No one went by here, sir, no one."

"We know they fled in this direction," said the leader coldly. "Are you sure they're not hiding in your house?"

This time he didn't wait for an answer, but pushed the frightened woman aside and motioned for two of his men to help make a search of the manor house.

There was resentment as well as fear in the boy's eyes as the soldiers' boots clattered over the stone floor of the low-ceilinged main room. Carrying candles whose light was reflected in pin points of red from the bright copper bottoms of the kitchen utensils on the wall, the soldiers made a quick tour of the lower floor and found nothing suspicious.

They then climbed the steep stairway to the second story where a thorough search of the bedrooms revealed no hidden "malignants," as the Puritans liked to call the adherents of the late King. Most of the windows on the upper floor had been carefully blocked to avoid payment of the unpopular window tax of that period.

"You are certain you didn't hear a band of about a dozen malignants ride by, Mistress—?" demanded the leader.

"My name is Mrs. Ayscough, sir. I assure you that I neither heard nor saw anyone go by during the past few weeks."

"Ayscough? I thought this was the Newton farm?"

"It is, sir," explained Mrs. Ayscough eagerly. "I'm the mother of Mrs. Newton—who is now Mrs. Smith. You see, my daughter is the wife of the Reverend Barnabas Smith of North Witham."

The leader wrote this information in a little book he had pulled from his breast pocket. "And who is this lad?" he asked with an inquiring glance at the boy.

Mrs. Ayscough placed herself squarely in front of her grandson, as if prepared to defend him at all costs.

"His name is Isaac Newton, sir. I am his grandmother and he lives with me." She held her breath as she looked squarely into the eyes of her questioner. Surely no one would want to harm her Isaac. Still, these were violent times, and one could never tell what form of cruelty might suggest itself to revengeful soldiers. . . .

The leader's manner softened. What damage could an old woman and a boy of eight, alone in a deserted area, do to the cause of the Commonwealth? he asked himself. He must waste no more time here. That there was a nest of malignants somewhere nearby—he was certain! And he was determined to exterminate that marauding band of Royalists even if it meant burning down half the farmhouses in this troublesome neighborhood!

"Do you have any horses?" he demanded suddenly as he snapped his book shut.

"No, sir. Some soldiers came this way a month ago and took our last one."

The leader shrugged his shoulders as if to say that it was too bad—but war was war. "Go through the barn," he called to his men. "Be sure to take precautions."

As he turned from the door he said meaningfully, "Remember, if you have lied to us, Mrs. Ayscough, the punishment will be painful, very painful." He paused for a moment before mounting his horse. "Anyone who sympathizes with malignants is an enemy of the Commonwealth," he cried.

By this time his men had completed the search of the barn, which was only a few hundred feet from the manor house, and found in it neither man nor beast. At a signal from the leader, the detachment wheeled back into the narrow dirt road and was off.

"It's all over, Isaac," exclaimed Mrs. Ayscough bravely as she tried hard to smile. She hugged her grandson, glad that the crisis was over—until the next time. "They didn't do us any harm, did they?"

The boy eyed his grandmother thoughtfully and did not answer. It was plain that he was disturbed not only by what had happened today but also by what might happen tomorrow or next week or next month. His childhood had been burdened with fears for the safety of his grandmother, his mother, himself. The raiders could terrify anyone, Mrs. Ayscough used to say to Isaac's mother—let alone a youngster awakened in the middle of the night and dragged from a warm bed by menacing soldiers!

Isaac understood what was taking place in the world around him. Cromwell was bent on destroying the scattered followers of the royal line—the Stuarts. He called them malignants; to the people, however, they were the Cavaliers, from their habit of wearing their hair in long curls. Though decisively defeated in the Civil War, the Cavaliers continued to fight guerrilla fashion from hiding places in the woods and swamps of the countryside. Every now and then they would emerge and harass the friends of the Commonwealth by burning down barns and destroying crops.

The Puritan followers of Cromwell, dubbed the Roundheads because of their closely cropped hair, countered by sending detachments of fast-moving cavalry to ferret out the rebellious Cavaliers. Thus every householder, every farmer, was suspect. If he aided either the Cavaliers or the Roundheads, punishment was sure to follow.

Mrs. Ayscough led her grandson back to his small bedroom

on the second floor. For a long time she sat alongside his bed in the darkness, holding his hand reassuringly. Soon she felt his grip relax. The boy was returning to the blessed world of sleep from which he had been snatched by the pounding on the door.

He was asleep now. Mrs. Ayscough tiptoed out of the room and went downstairs to sit and think, for she was too overwrought to sleep.

Isaac had stood up well once again, she said to herself. A sturdy lad! Those frightful raids could disorganize anybody. And the youngster had been exposed to them for years, alone with his grandmother on an isolated farm. The boy had courage!

"A terrible time in which to live!" sighed Mrs. Ayscough.

2

A HASTY VISIT

The news that Cromwell's men had stopped at Woolesthorpe reached Hannah Smith shortly after the raid, for country folk have ways of transmitting such information quickly. At dawn the anxious mother climbed into a small horse-drawn cart and was off to find out what had befallen her son and his grandma.

North Witham, where the Reverend Barnabas Smith had established his wife some six years before, was a tiny village about a mile from Woolesthorpe. Hannah Smith, with two small children, Mary and Benjamin, had had to make hasty arrangements for their care during this emergency. Fortunately she had managed to rouse a neighbor during the early morning hours; the latter, only too happy to be of help, had hurried to the Smith house before dawn to take care of the youngsters while their mother was away.

As the slow-moving cart joggled along, Hannah became more and more uneasy; her mind kept jumping from one dreadful possibility to another. To save herself from such agonizing thoughts, she forced herself to think of the unexpected series of events which had made her a wife, then a widow and finally a wife and mother again.

Her mind drifted back to her first marriage. Her husband

Isaac Newton had been stricken with a fatal illness; he died in the prime of life, at the age of thirty-six, not long after their marriage. Her son Isaac was born after his father had passed away. She could still see little Isaac! A puny infant—his head had to be supported by a bolster—and so tiny he could almost fit into a quart jug!

For two years Hannah Newton struggled alone with the farm, trying to support herself and her child. The manor house was the only valuable part of the estate left her by her late husband. The farm itself was poor, very poor. The income from it was never over thirty pounds a year—if she were lucky enough to find a farmer willing to lease it. And thirty pounds a year, even in those days, was scarcely sufficient to maintain a family. Isaac was only two years old then, and she had managed to keep the farm going by sheer will power—and hard work. Without help from her mother, she never could have carried on that long.

She recalled the day her brother James had brought her a marriage proposal from the Reverend Barnabas Smith of North Witham. A good husband was a precious asset in life, her family pointed out, and the Reverend would certainly be considerate of her. True, there was a difference in age—Hannah was about thirty-five and the Reverend nearing fifty at the time. But what did that matter? Barnabas Smith had remained a bachelor all these years out of choice; he was well to do and ready for matrimony.

A very kind man, a very kind man. Everyone had said that about Reverend Barnabas Smith—and had been proven right. He was eager to marry Hannah Newton, for the latter's name had become a byword for goodness in the small community. It was the widow Newton's local reputation as a hard-working, God-fearing, conscientious mother that had attracted the attention of the good Reverend.

There was nothing Reverend Smith would not agree to when negotiations got under way. At Hannah's request, her brother James Ayscough brought up the matter of a settlement on Isaac. The result was that Reverend Smith assigned to Isaac Newton a small parcel of land in near-by Sewstern. It was worth fifty pounds a year, and Hannah was pleased that her son Isaac would always have that to fall back on.

Hannah Smith snapped the reins to awaken the tired bony mare whose pace had gradually slackened. Her thoughts now slipped back to the most difficult part of the marriage arrangements: Isaac was to remain at Woolesthorpe with his grandmother. Not at home with his own mother as one might expect—but a mile away with Hannah's mother!

Many people had thought it strange, but what could she do? The great fear of her life had always been that her first-born might grow up in an atmosphere where he felt unwanted. Reverend Smith had never refused to let her bring Isaac into their new home. Still, Hannah realized that the former was not too enthusiastic about the idea. He wanted the feeling of a new household, a new life, without a stepson around—for the first year at least.

Hannah did not insist. Why not wait and see? she decided. It might be best for Isaac to stay at Woolesthrope for a while. With Grandma Ayscough prepared to take care of him there, and with her brother George willing to manage the farm, she could afford to please her new husband. And most important of all, Isaac was happy at Woolesthorpe and extremely fond of his grandmother.

By this time she had turned into the yard in front of the manor house. Isaac saw the cart and dashed out to greet his mother, closely followed by his smiling grandma.

"I'm so happy that they didn't harm you," cried Hannah as she threw her arms around her son. "Why did those terrible soldiers have to stop here? I heard about the raid early this morning and dropped everything to get here quickly."

"We were lucky," said Grandma. "All they did was to go through the house and barn. It was the fright of being wakened by them that I minded most."

"They visited a farm near the edge of North Witham, too," said Hannah Smith, "but that place didn't get off so easily. The soldiers took the poor farmer away with them because they said he had sold or given provisions to Wentworth's men."

"What a terrible thing to do to the poor man!" cried Grandma Ayscough indignantly. "Who will take care of his family now?"

"They say he'll be back in a day or two after paying a fine." Hannah kept eying her son worriedly. "Are you sure no bones are broken? They didn't touch you at all?"

Grandma laughed. "Isaac stood up very well. He glared harder at the soldiers than they did at him."

"Weren't you frightened, Isaac?" asked his mother.

The boy reflected for a few moments. "I suppose I was—but I figured they were after malignants and not me!"

Grandma let out a peal of laughter. "You see, Hannah, I have quite a helper here. Just wait till Isaac grows up. He's got the Ayscough stubborness in him—and he doesn't frighten easily."

"I hope these foolish wars will be over by then," said Hannah with a sigh. "By the way, I think Isaac is gaining weight. He's losing that frail look he used to have—thanks to you, Mother," she added gratefully.

"When boys get to a certain age they will eat and eat," noted Mrs. Ayscough modestly. "And there's nothing anyone can do to stop them from growing strong."

The two women chatted awhile about farm and home matters, with the visitor ever conscious of the responsibilities of her other household.

"Gracious!" exclaimed Hannah, jumping to her feet. I hadn't realized it was so late. I must get back to the children."

She climbed into the cart and was about to drive off when a thought occurred to her. "Why do you suppose the soldiers searched our house, Mother?"

Mrs. Ayscough became thoughtful. "It must be that someone directed them to our farm."

"But why to our farm?"

"For some reason," said Mrs. Ayscough worriedly, "we seem to be regarded as Cavalier sympathizers. Perhaps it is because of something we once said or failed to say. Anyway, that's how I would explain last night's visit—and also the one of last spring."

Hannah Smith looked troubled. It was true, she said to herself, it was true. The Newtons and the Smiths were suspected of being lukewarm to the Puritan cause. It was a mere suspicion but it was enough—even though neither family was particularly interested in the politics of the time.

Hannah Smith was aware that Lincolnshire was real "Cromwell country." It was one of the eastern counties from which the Protector had drawn so many of his God-fearing, Bible-quoting yeomen for his invincible New Model army.

It was dangerous to be suspect in an area where the Puritans were so strong. Hannah Smith had often prayed for peace to return once again to strife-torn England.

"I must get home," she cried. "The children are waiting for me."

The troubled mother kissed Isaac and Grandma, snapped the reins, and was off.

"I'll be down to see you on Saturday, Mother," called Isaac after her.

"Good!" shouted his mother, looking pleased. Isaac had been dropping in to see his half brother and half sister more and more frequently during the last few months. "I'm glad he's so fond of them," she said to herself. "How difficult it would be if Isaac had decided not to like my new family!"

3

THE BOARDER

The town of Grantham was about six miles from Woolesthorpe; and though its population did not quite reach a thousand at the time, it was nevertheless an important trading center for that part of Lincolnshire. On Saturdays the neighboring farmers would cart in their produce and spend the day bartering, buying or selling in the Grantham stalls.

Grantham was also important because of the Old King's School which had been established there in 1528, during the reign of Henry VIII. The school, whose headmaster was Henry Stokes, enjoyed an excellent reputation for preparing students for Cambridge and Oxford.

There was a house next to the George Inn, on High Street, which was occupied by Mr. Clark, an apothecary; and it happened that the apothecary's wife was a childhood friend of Isaac Newton's mother. It was the second marriage for Mrs. Clark; her daughter by her first marriage lived with the Clarks and provided the gaiety and excitement which the childless second marriage would otherwise have lacked.

On this particular day in September of 1654, Anne Storey, Mrs. Clark's daughter, was impatiently awaiting the arrival of a boarder—a boy boarder! For two weeks now the irrepressible ten-year-old girl, with the long brown curls and mischievous dark eyes, had been plying her parents with questions. She wanted to know more and more about the twelve-year-old boy who was going to live with the Clarks while attending the King's School.

"Why did he decide to come here?" she demanded. "There are ever so many people in Grantham he could have stayed with."

Mr. Clark eyed his stepdaughter with hidden amusement. "I'm sure it's because he knows you live here, Anne. There couldn't have been any other reason."

"You're teasing me!" cried Anne accusingly.

"As I have already explained to you," said Mrs. Clark patiently, "the boy's mother and I are old friends. She begged us to allow Isaac to live here because she felt we would be kind to him."

Anne went off on another tack. "Woolesthorpe is only a few miles from Grantham. I wonder why he has to board at all? Most of the boys who board live very far from the school. But Isaac—"

"It would mean walking twelve miles each day, and Mrs. Smith thought it would be too much for him—particularly in snowy or rainy weather. I think she was wise to arrange for her son to live near the school."

"What's he like, I wonder?" pursued the girl.

"Just be patient," said Mr. Clark with a smile. "Your curiosity will soon be satisfied. In a few hours you'll know all about him."

"I've seen the lad," confided Mrs. Clark. "Very quiet . . . doesn't chatter . . . the thoughtful type, I'd say. Isaac has been brought up by his grandmother on a lonely farm where he had few playmates. I guess that's why he's so quiet. He's not used to talking to people."

Anne looked shocked. She enjoyed the companionship of many friends and simply couldn't conceive of a happy life without girls of her own age to share her secrets and her laughter.

"Oh, he'll learn to talk here," laughed Mr. Clark, "if Anne ever gives him a chance."

"I'll let him talk if he wants to," said Anne gaily. "But Isaac has been to other schools. Why didn't he make friends there?" she persisted.

"Those were small day schools in Skillington and Stoke," explained her mother. "You can imagine what they were like —poor teachers and dull students. Most of the boys he went to school with were rough farm lads. Mrs. Smith wants her son to be a gentleman; that is why she is sending him to the King's School."

Anne Storey leaped from her chair and rushed to the window for the tenth time. "Oh, it's so exciting," she announced. "It's like getting a big brother all at once. I know I'm going to like him!"

"I'm sure you will, Anne," agreed her mother, trying not to smile. "Isaac Newton is a fine boy and comes from an honest, God-fearing family."

"Just remember to be quiet for the first few minutes—at least," cautioned Mr. Clark slyly, "or the poor lad might be frightened and become forever tongue-tied."

"I won't say a word, I won't say a word," promised Anne.

The Clarks, who were enjoying every minute of the waiting period, laughed delightedly.

Suddenly Anne let out a cry. Hannah Smith's cart had drawn up in front of the house!

"He's here!" the girl exclaimed, and would have rushed out the door to greet the young boarder if her mother had not restrained her.

"Wait a few minutes, dear," said Mrs. Clark. "Give them time to catch their breath."

Mrs. Clark walked to the window and looked out. The boy was busy removing several neatly tied bundles from the cart. Hannah Smith remained seated in the vehicle, resting from the morning's exertions. Finally Isaac proceeded to help his mother negotiate the high step from the cart to the street.

Mother and son threw curious glances at the outside of the Clark house. Mrs. Smith looked cheerful, as if congratulating herself at having solved the school problem for Isaac. The Clarks were wonderful people. Her son would be part of a happy family while attending an excellent school. A perfect arrangement!

Isaac, however, was far from joyful at the prospect of having to spend the next few years amidst strangers. Up to now he had always been more or less alone—and liked it. From this moment on he would have to think of other people. What would he say to them? What would he say to Mrs. Clark's daughter? What does one say to a girl, anyway?

Nor was the young man enthusiastic about studying at the King's School. It seemed to him that he had had enough of schooling. The one-room schools at Skillington and Stoke had taught him reading, writing and arithmetic. And he hadn't been particularly outstanding in any of these subjects. Why did he have to be bothered with more education—and in strange surroundings, too?

The reluctant scholar arranged his belongings in a neat pile beside the cart. He moved slowly, as if trying to postpone entering the house for as long as possible.

It was all the fault of his uncle, the Reverend William Ayscough, rector of Burton Coggles, a village near by. A firm believer in education, the Rector had managed to convince his sister Hannah that Isaac must be sent to a good school.

No sacrifice was too great, his uncle had argued, for Isaac could never hope to become a gentleman without good education. Since her husband had agreed to stand some of the expense of Isaac's board and tuition, Hannah Smith felt safe in giving her consent.

So now I'll be stuck here in Grantham with nothing to do but go to school, thought Isaac ruefully, as he stared at the ground. He thought longingly of the farm in Woolesthorpe, and of the manor house on the bank of the lovely river Witham. . . . Isaac had spent many happy summer afternoons lying in the tall grass which grew on the edge of that gentle, meandering stream.

The farm had been his whole world up to now. The plowing and the sheep-shearing . . . the shoeing of horses and the salting down of huge quantities of meat for the winter. Birds, flowers, fish, field mice—everything that possessed the magic quality called life—had always fascinated him.

There were so many things to watch, to puzzle over, on a farm! he said to himself. But what was there to do in a place like Grantham? A sudden thought struck him. Was his mother's decision due to his own bad habit of never completing a chore? But he simply couldn't help himself. There were so many puzzling questions he just had to find an answer to! He recalled the afternoon his mother had found him playing with an old wagon wheel. He had mounted it on a vertical axle, and was spinning it with a pebble on one of the wooden spokes. He had explained to his mother that the idea was to see how far the pebble would be thrown from different positions. But she didn't seem to understand. . . .

Hannah Smith finally woke her son out of his daydream.

"Let's take the things into the house," she said.

As soon as Isaac stooped to gather his belongings, Mrs. Clark decided that Mrs. Smith and her son had had enough time to themselves. She flung open the door and hurried out to greet them, closely followed by the excited Anne.

The moment after she had been introduced to the new boarder Anne took complete charge of the business of getting Isaac settled in his new home. While the grownups chatted, Anne and Isaac dragged the bundles of clothing and books and tools and treasured knickknacks to the latter's room on the second floor.

"This is your room, Isaac," said Anne, as she showed him into a large, neatly furnished room containing a bed, a dresser, bookshelves and a large oak table. "You'll use the table for your lessons," she added.

"Oh, yes," remarked the boy without enthusiasm. "Schoolwork."

"You'll like it here, won't you?" asked Anne confidentially.

Isaac thought hard. "Yes, I think so," he finally murmured.

Anne, a cheerful soul, was not easily affected by anyone's gloom. He's shy, she thought, but he'll get over it. Must give a person a funny feeling to have to live in a strange home—and with people one had never seen before. . . .

"Come," she said gaily, "I'll show you all through the house and back yard and shop and—"

"Shop?" Isaac looked surprised.

"Oh, yes. Father is an apothecary, you know. He has hundreds of vials with pretty chemicals and medicines in his shop. They have the queerest names, but they do make the most beautiful colors when added to water."

For the first time the new boarder showed an interest in what his new home had in store for him. Anne led him through the house and yard, chattering all the time to the astonishment and amusement of Isaac. Up to now he had never had an opportunity to speak to girls nearly his own age; it was going to be fun, lots of fun, to have one around, he decided.

Young Newton felt much more relaxed now. Perhaps living in town wouldn't be too dull, after all. Then came the tour of inspection through the apothecary's shop. The boy's eyes widenened. This was a new world. a mysterious and exciting world! Mercurius calcinatus . . . aqua regia . . . oil of vitriol . . . sulphur . . . mercury . . . spirits of wine . . . salts of tartar . . . white hellebore . . . oil of aniseeds . . . oyle pink . . . cinnabar. . . .

Anne wondered why her new friend's eyes were shining so. The names and colors of the chemicals on the shelves were interesting—but not that exciting!

"I'd like to know more about what's in those vials," said Isaac. "Your father has so many wonderful things in his shop —so many."

"Yes, and he will tell you all about them if you ask him. He's very kind and never loses his temper."

"I'll have to get a book which tells about the substances on the shelves," murmured Isaac. "I have so many questions to ask. I'm afraid your father will lose patience with me."

"No, he won't," protested Anne. "Anyway, we have piles and piles of books in the attic. There must be a book there about the things in those vials."

Books . . . chemistry . . . lots of leisure! The young boarder began to look positively cheerful. No matter how dull school might prove, the Clark house would make up for everything. He could read and build things and learn about those mysterious chemicals. And he wouldn't feel lonely, at all. No—not with the gay Anne Storey around to talk to and laugh with.

When they finally reached Anne's room, she proudly pointed out to him her collection of rag dolls and also some embroidered pieces she had made. Isaac looked properly impressed with her achievements.

"I had a sort of toy table on which I used to serve tea to

my friends when they came to visit me. But someone sat on it and now it's useless; the legs are broken."

Isaac smiled. "I brought some of my tools with me. I'll find a good pine board and make new legs for it."

That was all Anne wanted to hear! A real big brother in her home at last! He could even build things for her! She was already bursting with pride over her latest "acquisition," and couldn't wait to tell her friends about her good luck!

In a few minutes she outlined a number of construction projects on which she was *sure* Isaac would enjoy working. He listened with a half-smile and wondered if his charming friend would remember half of them the next day. However, Isaac solemnly promised to get started on them as soon as possible—if Anne would tell him which were most important to her. He loved to fashion things and, as it turned out, spent many an afternoon sawing and hammering to please the enthusiastic Anne.

There was a call from Mrs. Clark. Hannah Smith had to leave. It would take time to get back to North Witham where her children were impatiently awaiting her return.

"You'll like it here, Isaac," said his mother. "I'm sure you will. You couldn't find a nicer family to live with."

Isaac nodded and seemed to be rather cheerful about it all —to his mother's surprise. "Yes, Mother, I'll like it here. This house is full of so many interesting things."

"I showed him dozens and dozens of chemicals on the shelves of Father's shop," exclaimed Anne. "And he wants to know all about them."

"I'll be happy to help him learn," said Mr. Clark, putting his hand on the boy's shoulder." Perhaps Isaac will even help me in the shop."

The new boarder looked pleased and threw the apothecary

a grateful glance. "I'd like to learn enough to help you, sir," he murmured.

Hannah Smith rose to her feet. "I can't tell you how happy you and Mr. Clark have made me by consenting to take Isaac," she said as she kissed Mrs. Clark.

"Don't thank us, Hannah. We'll enjoy having Isaac live with us. I know we will. And remember now—no worrying! We'll feed Isaac and care for him as if he were our own."

"He won't give you any trouble over food," laughed Mrs. Smith. "Isaac will eat anything you put in front of him. You won't have to fuss at all. All food tastes the same to him!"

Isaac accompanied his mother to the waiting cart and helped her in.

"I'll drop in to see you on Saturday when we go to market," she said. "Good-by, Isaac!" she leaned over, kissed her son and was off.

The boy stood and watched the slow-moving vehicle bumping down the rutted street until it was out of sight. Slowly he walked back to the house. A new life had begun for him. He was no longer a farm boy!

4

QUIET YEARS

Young Newton sat at one of the rear benches of his new school carefully carving his initials into the paneled wall. Since many others had done so before him, the youth from Woolesthrope decided that he, too, must leave his impression on the wall for posterity.

The main building of the King's School, with its vaulted ceiling, seemed to him more like a church than a classroom. In the middle of the huge room were several long tables at which sat rows of boys. Flanking the student benches were two raised pews from which the tutors could keep a close check on the activities of their charges.

Isaac had been at the school only a few months, and on this particular morning he was in a real turmoil. Up to now he had sat at his bench in a daydreaming state, counting the hours before he'd be back at the apothecary's shop. Once school was out, he would wake up; there were things to construct, books to read—and ever so much to learn about chemistry from the fatherly Mr. Clark.

The young scholar was not at all bothered by the fact that he was in next to the lowest form in the school—and the lowest boy in that, too! Isaac just didn't care about school, not even the King's School.

He kept pushing his jackknife into the wall savagely, as a relief from the fury and anger which were overflowing inside. Ever since the term began, he had been badgered by one of the boys in his own form. For some reason—or no reason—the boy, much taller and stronger than Isaac, had taken a violent dislike to the slow student from Woolesthorpe.

Since young Newton was apparently duller than the dull bully, the latter began to regard the newcomer as fair game. It started out as little more than an occasional push or cuff, but soon became progressively worse—and more painful—for poor Isaac.

Bullies were nothing new to Isaac Newton, for he had gone to school with rough farm lads at Skillington and Stoke. More than once he had witnessed the inevitable tormenting of the weak by the strong. Fortunately, the bigger boys had seldom picked on the inoffensive Newton; there was something sturdy—almost stubborn—about him, and this seemed to discourage muscular youngsters in search of easy victims. It was plain to most that although Isaac was a quiet, dreamy boy who stayed by himself, it was inadvisable to try to push him too far; there was always the possibility that he might lash back violently if driven beyond a certain point.

But this blusterer at the King's School was different. Very stupidly he mistook Isaac's lack of interest in the schoolyard sports for fear or timidity. On this very day of the initial carving, for instance, he had shown his contempt for the new boy by giving Isaac a nasty kick when the two had met on the way to school.

All day Isaac kept seething at the insult, the most painful insult. It was wholly uncalled for . . . he hadn't said a word to his swaggering schoolmate. When he shut his eyes, Isaac could still see the gleeful look on his tormentor's face when the victim doubled up with pain.

The more the smaller boy thought about the injustice of the blow, the more furious he became. By the end of the long day, Isaac had resolved that the bully must be punished! It didn't matter that the "enemy" was taller and stronger. He must be taught a lesson and Isaac was determined to do the teaching!

Directly at dismissal, young Newton kept doggedly at the heels of his tormentor. He wanted to be sure that he did not get away. The moment they reached the churchyard in front of the school, which served as a playground, Isaac ran ahead and planted himself squarely in the path of his antagonist.

"I want to fight you," he said quietly, throwing his books to the ground and bringing his clenched fists up to position.

The blusterer looked surprised and somewhat uncomfortable. "Fight me? What for?"

"Because you kicked me!" announced Isaac belligerently.

The bully tried to laugh it off. "Oh, that? So it did hurt you? Good! Run along farm boy and find someone your own little size to fight with!"

Isaac's answer was to rain a dozen furious but effective blows on the face and body of his tormentor. The lad from Woolesthorpe was doing well; anger and outraged dignity added power and snap to his attack. The shy, dreaming reserved attitude of the schoolboy Newton had disappeared. He was giving all he had to the business at hand.

Taken aback by the fury of Newton's blows, the flustered bully looked around for a way out. That new boy could certainly hurt! For a few moments it appeared that the bigger boy was about to take to his heels and take his chances on being able to laugh off the encounter afterward as a sort of joke.

As it happened, Young Stokes, a student at the school and the son of the Headmaster, sauntered up at just the right moment. He knew the bully by reputation, and more than once had caught him beating smaller boys. Stokes quickly decided that here was the golden opportunity of which he simply had to take advantage.

"A fight, a fight! Let's watch the fight!" he cried loud enough to attract the attention of ten or twelve boys who were busy playing ball in the schoolyard.

In no time at all, the antagonists were encircled by an excited and enthusiastic audience. The bully was cornered; he had to fight now—even though he had no stomach for physical combat.

With Stokes egging the fighters on, and the onlookers shouting advice, the battle was resumed. The resentful and angry Isaac hit out so hard and mercilessly at the head and chest of the blusterer that the latter suddenly became an almost helpless target. Soon the bully lost his balance and was down!

The Headmaster's son was unable to hide his glee at the surprising outcome of the fight. Stretched out on the ground was the bully, pretending to be hurt in order to escape further humiliation—and punishment!

"Rub his nose in the dirt, Newton, rub his nose in the dirt!" cried young Stokes, forgetting his own delicate position as the Headmaster's son. "He's a coward . . . he won't fight!"

Acting on this suggestion, Isaac proceeded to add insult to injury by pushing the bully's face hard into the mud of the churchyard.

Amidst the laughter of the bystanders, Newton's tormentor struggled to his feet and took to his heels, and from then on he was careful to steer clear of the quiet farm boy from Woolesthorpe. And at the King's School, Isaac Newton's position among the boys was now secure. If he didn't wish to engage in sports with the others, that was his own business. Everyone realized that young Newton could take care of himself—and that was all that counted.

Isaac's experience with the bully had a curious effect on his attitude toward his schoolwork. He realized that he had managed to beat the blusterer by a sudden display of will power and strength. Why couldn't he do the same in his studies? And so, for the first time in his school life, young Newton acquired a goal: he wasn't going to be the lowest in his form any longer!

As a result he began to apply himself to his schoolwork with a single-mindedness and tenacity that surprised everyone. Headmaster Stokes watched with undisguised delight as his once "lowest" student began to display an astonishing mastery of almost every subject in the school curriculum.

"Newton has changed so. He's not the same boy he was when he first came to us," the Headmaster said to the tutors. "I dare say he will be first scholar in a few years if he keeps it up," the enthusiastic schoolmaster predicted.

The years spent in Grantham were golden years for young Isaac Newton. Each day was full to overflowing with activity; there were not enough hours for his reading, model-making, kite-flying, gadget-making and experimenting with chemicals.

He spent his school vacations on the Woolesthorpe farm and made weekly visits to North Witham to see his mother and half brother and half sisters, of whom there were three by this time. Since these precious years were completely free from worry, the happy Isaac devoted every minute of his waking day to satisfying the intense and far-reaching curiosity of his restless mind.

"What will it be tonight?" Mr. Clark asked, with an approving smile. "Another kite with a lantern tied to its tail to scare the neighboring farmers out of their wits? Or an improvement of your sundial? Or more furniture for Anne?"

"More furniture for me!" Anne cried.

"Let Isaac speak for himself. Oh, yes, I forgot—would you like to help me mix some medicine in the shop, Isaac?" Mr. Clark smiled and waited for the boy's reaction.

"I'd like that, Mr. Clark," murmured Isaac, throwing an apologetic glance at Anne.

"Very well," said the girl firmly. "But don't forget that tomorrow night will be furniture night, Isaac. You're always playing with those old chemicals!"

Isaac loved the apothecary's shop best of all. Mr. Clark had taught him how to roll pills and prepare certain medicines. They had long discussions about mercury and acids and how to form beautiful crystals. The boy had acquired considerable information from his avid reading of the science books in the Clark attic; and the apothecary enjoyed feeding the ever-hungry mind of the youth with facts and explanations concerning chemistry.

One day Isaac came across some workmen who were engaged in erecting a windmill on the road to Gunnerby, not far from Grantham. Isaac was fascinated. He must make a scale model of the windmill, he said to himself. Anne could play with it. A small windmill was just the thing she'd enjoy.

To the amusement of the workmen, Isaac measured and inspected and measured. When he got home, he told Anne about his new project and she was delighted. The lad went to work with saw and hammer, and in a few days turned out an almost perfect replica of the Gunnerby mill! First he mounted it on the roof of the Clark house; and when he tired of that, he amused the shrieking Anne by taking it down and cleverly installing a mouse, which he called the miller, in the little windmill to supply the power to make it turn!

His fast-growing brain was already so crammed with projects and ideas and puzzling thoughts that he began to display the absent-mindedness which was to become legendary in later life.

Anne never tired of teasing Isaac about an incident on Spittlegate Hill near Grantham. The story, which had to do with absent-mindedness, had managed to amuse the neighborhood for many weeks.

"Why did you bother holding onto the bridle?" Anne would ask mischievously. It had become a sort of table game for the Clark household.

Isaac never failed to give her the answers she expected. It was fun to see Anne's eyes crinkle up, as if unable to contain the laughter that filled them.

"I felt sorry for my old nag and thought it would be easier for him to be led up Spittlegate Hill. I didn't think he could reach the summit with me on his back," he exclaimed soberly.

"But why did you have to carry the bridle in your hand? Wasn't the horse strong enough to bear his own bridle?" asked the girl innocently.

Isaac tried to hide his amusement. "You see—I started off with the reins in my hand, expecting to lead my horse up the steep hill. It was only *after* I got to the top that I realized that all I had was the horse's bridle."

"And what had happened to the horse?" continued Anne.

"He just strayed off," said Isaac patiently. "It took me about an hour to find him."

"And you didn't know that the horse had slipped his bridle and wandered off?" asked Anne unbelievingly.

"No," said Isaac seriously. "I honestly didn't know it."

"How could you not know it!" cried Anne. "Anyone else

would have known the difference between leading a bridle up a hill and leading a horse up a hill."

"Anyone?" said Isaac dubiously. "Perhaps. But I didn't." He reflected for a few seconds and then added, "I suppose I was thinking of other things."

Anne let out a shriek of laughter. "You suppose? You suppose? When isn't Isaac Newton thinking of other things!"

"I guess I am absent-minded," said Isaac seriously. "I often wonder how other people manage to keep their minds on what they are doing. I can't—no matter how I try."

"Don't feel badly about it," Anne told him comfortingly. "I think it's fun to be absent-minded. It shows you have lots to think about. I want you to stay just the way you are—absent-mindedness and all!"

Anne let out another peal of laughter, looked at him fondly for a moment, then ran out of the room. Isaac remained standing, lost in thought. He wondered at the strange antics of girls. . . .

5

THE IMPOSSIBLE FARMER

In 1656 Reverend Barnabas Smith died, and Isaac Newton's mother found herself a widow for the second time. At a family conference after the funeral it was decided that she should leave the rectory and go back to Woolesthorpe with her three children—Benjamin, Mary and Hannah.

The problem of providing for the young family was eased considerably by the fact that the late Reverend had left his wife an estate worth five hundred pounds a year. If Hannah Smith lived on the Woolesthorpe farm and managed her household prudently, her family would never know want.

"I'll leave Isaac at Grantham to finish his schooling," Mrs. Smith announced. "He's been at the King's School only two years, and a fourteen-year-old boy is still too interested in play to be of any great help on a farm."

Her brother, the stout and studious-looking Reverend William Ayscough was pleased with Hannah's decision. "Very wise, very wise," he commented. "Isaac is doing exceedingly well at school, according to Mr. Stokes. It would be a serious mistake to withdraw him at this point." Though he had never expressed the thought, the Reverend secretly hoped that Isaac would some day enter the Church.

Hannah Smith was always happy when her son was praised. "I'll manage without him, William, until he's much older," she said. Her eyes paused a moment on the three restless children running about the kitchen, and she added, "I'll let Isaac finish at the King's School—if God gives me strength!"

Isaac, who possessed more than average youthful blindness to the problems of parents, was happy over his mother's decision. Mrs. Smith had informed her son about his late stepfather's estate, and Isaac imagined it could easily take care of all of her needs.

But Anne Storey was the most relieved person of all! She was always fearful of losing the playmate whose ingenious hands and insatiable scientific curiosity had made life in the Clark house so exciting.

"I'm so glad he's going to stay on," she kept repeating to her mother. "What would we do without Isaac around?"

"Hannah Smith is a good mother and is trying to do her best for Isaac," observed Mrs. Clark thoughtfully. "She'll be alone with the children on the farm. Grandma Ayscough is too old now to be of any help. And Isaac's uncle George, who has his own farm to care for, can spare little time for Woolesthorpe."

And so Isaac Newton remained at the King's School for two more years, completely absorbed by his chemistry and model-making and studies. He particularly loved those long rainy days when he would read book after book of the fascinating collection of odds and ends in the Clark attic. Each book seemed to open new horizons; his mind, never at rest, always wanted to understand more and more.

While her son was having thrilling experiences with his

sundials and minerals and birdlore, Hannah Smith was having her difficulties at Woolesthorpe. Cromwell had divided England into eleven areas, each under a major general whose duty it was to "preserve order." In practice this meant the taxation of Royalist sympathizers, the punishment of those caught swearing or gambling or tippling, and the close supervision of the religious customs of the people.

The countryside was soon in turmoil. Cromwell's troops were everywhere, and no man could trust his neighbor. There was no appeal from the arbitrary decisions of the major generals. In some cases, aged men were transported to island plantations on the mere suspicion of being enemies of the Commonwealth.

Mrs. Smith found it harder and harder to get along. Hired help was almost impossible to obtain; wages rose and trade dropped to a dangerously low level throughout the country. It seemed to Isaac's mother that nothing was secure any more, not even the income she had inherited from her late husband.

After the death of his stepfather, Isaac's visits to Woolesthorpe became more and more frequent. The Clarks didn't ask the boy any questions, for they suspected what was troubling their young boarder.

"I sometimes think," confided Isaac to Anne on one of these rare occasions when he discussed his personal problems, "that I should be on the farm helping my mother. She's been looking very tired lately. There's so much for her to do, and it's hard to get anyone to work on a farm these days."

"But you can't leave school!" cried Anne. "You'd be useless on the farm, Isaac. You're—you're just not suited to farm work."

"I can try," answered Isaac, with a troubled look, as he turned once again to the book he had been reading.

What the Clarks had expected—and Anne Storey had

feared—happened. At the end of the June term in 1658, Isaac returned from an overnight visit to Woolesthorpe with the news that he was leaving the King's School. It was two years since his stepfather had died; Isaac was now fifteen and a half years old, and had boarded at Grantham for almost four years.

Mrs. Clark had gotten the story from Hannah Smith the week before. The widow simply couldn't hold out any longer, conditions being what they were. At her son's urgings, she had decided to take him out of school. Mr. Stokes, the Headmaster, didn't like the idea at all, and had tried to dissuade the widow by offering to forgo the next year's tuition.

"Mr. Stokes pleaded so for Isaac that I almost changed my mind," confessed Hannah to Mrs. Clark. "But it's so hard to run a farm without a man around. And Isaac insists that he's strong enough now to do a man's work."

Young Newton himself did not regard the step as tragic at all. He came from a long line of yeoman farmers, and had never had his heart set on a college education. At the King's School he had often heard the boys speak of entering Oxford or Cambridge, but such thoughts had never concerned him because he had neither academic nor social ambitions. His intense curiosity and reflective turn of mind made him an omnivorous reader and self-activated learner. His only ambition was to understand more and more.

However, Isaac was disturbed by the necessity of leaving the Clarks, whom he had learned to love—particularly Anne Storey. The four happy years spent under the same roof had drawn the two young people closer than they had realized.

"It isn't good-by, Anne," he said to her nervously, the day he left the Clarks. "We'll be seeing each other often, because I'll be carting things to the market every week."

"Yes, yes, of course," mumbled Anne, trying bravely to

hold back her tears. "You'll be only a few miles away. And you'll visit us—and—perhaps I'll see you at Woolesthorpe every now and then."

The shy country lad looked down, not knowing what to say. He was suddenly conscious of how much Anne's companionship meant to him. Anne and Isaac had become attached to each other over the years; their separation was a painful experience.

Isaac turned and walked out the door quickly, as if he found the parting too disturbing to bear.

Back at Woolesthorpe, the young farmer started off manfully determined to work as hard as any hired man—even though he was not quite sixteen. He felt strong and could see no reason why he shouldn't be a great help to his mother, who had the house to take care of, plus cooking and sewing and laundering for a family of small children.

Alas! it just didn't turn out as both Isaac and his mother had hoped. Each day would find the new farmer full of a determination of which little remained after a few hours. There was always the little notebook in which he would jot down a description of a bird or a mineral; sometimes he would push his chores aside and spend an afternoon in the fields drawing with charcoal. On other occasions the young farmer would just sit, lost in thought!

It wasn't long before his mother was wringing her hands—in private—wondering what she had gained by having Isaac around as a helper.

"I can't figure out what goes on in his mind!" she would say to Grandma Ayscough. "He seems to be absorbed in everything except farm work."

"Be patient," counseled Grandma, who always had a warm spot in her heart for the boy she had helped raise from a feeble child to a sturdy youth. "After all, he's been with books for a long time. If you're patient with him, he'll forget his books and become a farmer. You must not expect too much at first."

Mrs. Smith became even more certain that she had made a mistake in withdrawing her son from school when she witnessed Isaac's strange behavior during a violent storm in the autumn of 1658.

This memorable storm swept over England a few days before the death of Cromwell. It's fury caused vast destruction throughout the country: ancient trees were uprooted, chimneys toppled and ships overturned. Those who loved the ailing Cromwell regarded the storm as a portent of the evil to come with the passing of the Lord High Protector; those who hated the dying leader of the Puritans saw in the same storm a sign that tyranny was about to be overthrown, and that English liberties would soon be restored.

"Go to the barn, Isaac," his mother had directed when the wind began to blow fiercely, "and latch the door before it is torn off."

"Yes, Mother," said her son eagerly, as he hastened to comply.

About half an hour later, Hannah Smith noticed that Isaac had not returned from his five-minute chore. She began to worry. The wind was howling and the sky was ominously black. She wondered if her son had met with an accident. Seizing her shawl, she rushed to the barn to find out what was keeping the young farmer.

There she saw her dutiful son completely absorbed in a game: he would climb up to the barn window and then jump to the ground, each time marking the spot at which he landed.

She ran around the corner of the building. There was the heavy barn door—twisted off its hinges and broken into three parts by the howling wind!

"What are you doing, Isaac?" asked his mother gently, after she had watched his antics for a few moments.

Isaac looked embarrassed, for he suddenly remembered that he had been sent on an errand; he looked through the window of the barn and saw the broken door. "I'm sorry, Mother," he said. "I should have attended to the door first instead of trying to measure the force of the wind by seeing how far it carried me when I jumped from the window ledge."

"I think you'd better go back to the house, Isaac. It's beginning to rain."

What could she do with her Isaac? the widow asked herself hopelessly. He was a good son and did try to ease her burden. There was nothing he would not do cheerfully—or begin to do—if she requested it of him. But that was where it ended. The lad was simply incapable of resisting a thought, an idea or an interest. He was just as eager to learn about the mixing of pigments as about phonetic spelling!

School or no school, the youth continued to grow mentally; eagerly he followed his intellectual curiosity wherever it led him. His notebook at that time was carefully divided into sixteen sections—minerals, birds, arts and trades, etc.

As the months slipped by there was little noticeable change in Isaac's adjustment—or lack of adjustment—to farm routine. There were days when he managed to stick to a job without daydreaming or fits of reading; but these were few and far between.

After waiting patiently almost two years for her absent-minded son to develop into an efficient farmer, Hannah Smith came to the conclusion that she was waging a hopeless struggle against human nature.

"Do you think I ought to let him go back to Grantham to finish his schooling? she asked her brother, the Reverend

William Ayscough, who was still keenly interested in Isaac's future.

Her brother thought for a while before answering. He must not tell Hannah that he had once found Isaac sitting under a hedge at the foot of Spittlegate Hill reading a mathematics book! The Reverend had decided, right then and there, that Hannah had a real scholar in her family but didn't know it! Here was the youth absorbed in a book when he should have been in the Grantham stalls trying to sell the produce of the Woolesthorpe farm for as much as possible. And Isaac's explanation was that the hired man was taking care of the bartering and selling and knew a great deal about such things—and didn't need the help of a beginner!

The Rector looked at his sister sympathetically. "As you know, Hannah, the lad simply cannot help himself. He is what God made him, and he'll be just that regardless of whether he tries to be a farmer or sailor or tradesman. We must not be harsh with Isaac. His inclinations are all for reading, learning, thinking. Indeed, we should be thankful that the Lord has given your son an extraordinary interest in the things of the mind."

Hannah was pleased at the high opinion her brother had of Isaac. Even though her son had proved a failure as a farmer, he remained her favorite child and she was forever making excuses for his daydreaming and absent-mindedness. "You think, then, that he ought to finish his schooling?"

Her brother nodded. "I think so. The love of learning is seldom found in the young. And when a lad has it as strongly as Isaac, it would be wrong to deprive him of an education. He must finish at the King's School and then go on to Trinity College."

Hannah Smith jumped. Trinity College! That was in Cambridge. She hadn't thought that far ahead. Was her brother

William saying that because he himself had been educated there? And how could she afford the expense of a college education?

"I'm not sure about Trinity, William," she said, somewhat worried at the problem that was so certain to come up in the future. "First we'll send Isaac back to Grantham in the fall."

"A very wise decision," commented her brother. "There's no profit in harnessing an eagle to a plow."

The upshot was that in September of 1660, Isaac Newton found himself living with the Clarks again, after an absence of almost two years. The Headmaster was overjoyed, the Clarks happy, and Anne Storey thrilled.

At about this period Isaac's mother began to feel more secure financially. Charles II had been called to the throne upon the death of Cromwell; and the period in English history known as the Restoration was now ushered in. The new king promised religious toleration and a general pardon to the followers of Cromwell. Enthusiastic crowds were at hand to greet the arrival of the new monarch at Dover. There was a general feeling of optimism throughout the country; the people were sure that the next few years would bring good times, now that the irksome restrictions of the Puritans were things of the past.

Isaac worked hard at his studies the year he returned to school. Mr. Stokes was determined that his prize student should learn enough Latin, Greek, classical history, biblical history, grammar and Hebrew to qualify for admission to Trinity College, Cambridge University.

His teachers found that the two years of apparent idleness had increased rather than diminished Isaac Newton's intellectual power. His mind was more mature now; the leisure, the lack of external pressure, the habit of shifting his interest from one field to another had not hurt him at all. On the contrary, the long period of mental freedom had served to enrich the soil in which so many magnificent ideas were soon to take root. Never had two years of youthful idleness proved less "idle"!

Reverend William Ayscough, aided by the co-operative Mr. Stokes, handled the college problem with great skill. They didn't waste time discussing the pros and cons of a college education with Isaac's mother at all; the two men simply took it for granted that Isaac Newton would go from the King's School to Trinity College. Soon Hannah Smith caught the idea that any other course for her gifted son was simply unthinkable!

"Once he is admitted to Trinity, things will take care of themselves," her brother would say cheerfully. "We'll get him a scholarship which will ease the financial burden for you considerably."

By this time Hannah had become conscious of her son's unusual qualities: Isaac was one to be cared for, prized. And when the Headmaster and her brother revealed the plans they had in mind for Isaac, Mrs. Smith was pleased and offered no objections.

On Isaac Newton's last day at the King's School, the beaming widow heard Mr. Stokes laud her son's character and scholarship to the skies before a large gathering of parents and students. Her eyes filled with tears when the Headmaster, obviously overcome by emotion, went on to hold up Isaac as the scholar of whom the school was most proud. . . .

Reverend William Ayscough was happy that day, too, for his nephew Isaac had just received his notice of acceptance from Trinity College. Yes, the lad was going to get a college education!

6

TRINITY COLLEGE

On June 5, 1661, Isaac Newton was admitted to Trinity College, Cambridge University. It took him several days to recover from the arduous two-day trip by coach; the distance from Woolesthorpe to Cambridge was only about fifty miles, but the terrible road conditions, plus the constant fear of highwaymen, made traveling a trying experience.

Newton missed his mother, and was lonely for Anne and the happy bustling family life at Woolesthorpe. He kept thinking of those wonderful years at Grantham, and of the vivacious and charming girl whose companionship had meant so much to him. Anne had taken his departure hard; the memory of her weeping at their parting remained with him for a long time afterward.

Here at Cambridge he knew only two Fellows to whom his uncle, the Reverend Ayscough, had given him letters of introduction. Since he was poor, Newton lived a life apart from the young men of wit and fashion who had been prepared for Cambridge at the great English public schools. There were only a few Sizars among the forty students admitted with Newton that year—and he was one of them. To be a Sizar meant that a student had to perform such menial services as running errands and waiting on his tutor in exchange for board and tuition.

The youth from Woolesthorpe, brought up far from the world of the gay blades around him, looked at his associates with the eyes of a shy, suspicious country boy. He realized that socially he counted for little, since he was the son of a small farmer or yeoman. True, his family owned a manor house; but even that had been acquired as part of a parcel of land his grandfather had purchased at Woolesthorpe about a hundred years ago. It was clear that there was no social prestige to be squeezed from Isaac Newton's background.

In a short time, however, he managed to forget all about his insignificant position among his fellow students. As soon as he discovered the precious books in the college library, Newton realized what a golden opportunity Trinity offered the inquiring mind. It was going to be like Grantham—only better! The wonderful manuscripts in the college library went far beyond the collection of books in the Clark attic.

At first he was unable to do any studying or reading in his own room because of a noisy roommate. Trinity was overcrowded at that time, for the two wings of Neville's Court had not yet been completed. As it was, Newton was fortunate in having to share his room with only one person; there were cases where three or four students were assigned to one room during that year. At any rate, during the first few months Newton cetainly did not find at Trinity the peace and tranquility of which his uncle had often spoken.

Driven from his room by the noise one night, he wandered aimlessly through the Great Court, as the college quadrangle was called, wondering how much longer he would have to put up with his roistering roommate. Out of the corner of his eye he noticed another student in the quadrangle, also in no hurry to go anywhere.

Finally the young man approached and eyed him quizzically. "Driven out of your room, too, Newton?"

He recognized the speaker as John Wickins, a divinity student.

"Yes," said Newton. "I found it, as usual, too noisy for reading or study."

"Sounds like my roommmate: too much money, too many friends and absolutely no understanding of how much ale a mortal can safely swallow."

Newton smiled. "I have to escape to the open air often, too often. It will be a great relief to me to get rid of this roommate—if I ever do."

"I understand how you feel," said Wickins sympathetically. "I—I—" He stopped suddenly. "I just got an idea, Newton."

"What is it?"

"Why can't we get your roommate to live with mine? Then you and I will be able to room together. Since our noisy friends are apparently of the same mind, they should be pleased with one another."

"An excellent suggestion!" observed Newton. "Do you think it can be arranged?"

"We can try," answered Wickins optimistically.

John Wickins wasted no time. He approached the college officials tactfully on the subject of the exchange of roommates, and soon extracted a promise that his unusual request would receive consideration. Before long the switch was carried out with no ill feelings on the part of the high-living pair who were placed in one room. Newton and Wickins got along very well and continued to room together for several years.

There was nothing outstanding about Newton's college work during his first years at Trinity. He was just another Sizar as far as his teachers and fellow students were concerned. Newton himself was keenly disappointed at the absence of science from the college curriculum. Cambridge, at that time, was still concentrating on philosophy and theology; like Oxford, it was far behind the universities on the Continent, where the ideas of Galileo, Descartes and Kepler were beginning to attract the attention of some of the finest minds in the academic world.

"Tell me about Trinity," said his mother eagerly, on his first visit home at the end of the first term.

"Well," began Isaac slowly, "my tutor is Mr. Pulleyn, an excellent scholar. He is in charge of my studies and is very kind. It was he who excused me from attending the lectures in logic. He said I had acquired a good grasp of that subject from reading the logic book Uncle William gave me when I left Woolesthorpe."

"What do you study, then?" asked his mother curiously.

"The usual subjects—Latin, Greek, the Bible, arithmetic, Euclid, trigonometry. And I must not forget the lectures on the Copernican system—they're the most fascinating of all!"

The widow seemed satisfied with her son's list of studies—even though some did sound strange to her. However, if Trinity demanded and her Isaac liked those subjects—then they were certainly acceptable to her!

"You're not working too hard, Isaac?" she asked anxiously.

Her son laughed. "No, Mother, not at all. I have nothing to do but read and study. The college has a wonderful library in which I could spend the rest of my life and still have much to learn."

What he didn't tell his mother was that he had been spending more time reading everything he could lay his hands on than in doing his college work. Newton was having the time of his life exploring the world of learning. He wanted to taste of everything, and he turned to each new field with breathless interest. Some subjects he would push aside after a brief sampling; others he would bite into with a power and concentration unusual in one so young. To Isaac Newton, almost all knowledge during this glorious period had a gleam, a freshness, that made his mind almost dance with joy.

He looked forward to his visits to Woolesthorpe—and Grantham. Newton needed the warmth of his family and friends; after long stretches of intellectual labors at Trinity, he eagerly counted the weeks to vacation time. Though the young scholar had little money to spare, he seldom returned home without little presents for the children at Woolesthorpe —and for Anne Storey.

Anne would listen thoughtfully to her admirer's account of what Trinity was like, and wonder if he still felt the same way about her. When Isaac had first left for college, there was a sort of "understanding" between them. Someday they would be married. When? Neither Anne nor Isaac could answer that because the decision to send the latter to college had unsettled all of their plans.

"You like it at Trinity?" asked Anne, after he had told of the various Fellows at the College, and the strange behavior of some. It seemed that the Puritans, when they were in power, had ejected a number of the ablest Fellows from Trinity; and of those who remained quite a few had lost interest in the studies they were supposed to pursue. In fact, Mr. Pulleyn, Isaac's tutor, had hinted that Trinity was not what it used to be. Too much interference by the Crown . . . too many appointments based on favoritism rather than ability.

"Yes," said Isaac, "I do like it. There is something wonderful about the atmosphere. It is so withdrawn from the world. It must be grand to be a Fellow and have nothing to think about but books and ideas."

Anne tried to be gay after that, but it was plain that she

was troubled by Isaac's fascination for the academic life. Mr. Clark had once told her that Fellows were not permitted to marry. She wondered if Isaac's attitude meant that they would have to wait until the seven-year Fellowship period was over before they could think of marriage? And would he ever desire matrimony if the bachelor's life of a Fellow seemed so attractive to him now? Anne began to feel insecure about the future.

Back at Cambridge in the spring of 1663, Wickins burst into their room, one afternoon, all excited about the news he had just heard.

"Newton—do you know who is coming to Trinity beginning with the Easter term?" he cried.

"No," mumbled his roommate without looking up from his reading.

"Isaac Barrow, the great Dr. Barrow!" announced Wickins, all aglow. "Do you realize that Barrow is one of the great masters of the English language. What magnificent sermons that man can preach! And he's not only a minister but also one of the greatest living scientists and mathematicians!"

Newton pricked up his ears. A mathematician? A scientist? This was really great news!

More information was soon forthcoming from the enthusiastic Wickins. "Barrow has just been appointed to the chair of mathematics recently established by Henry Lucas . . . Barrow will become the first Lucasion professor of mathematics at Cambridge. And beginning with the Easter term he will lecture on natural philosophy—particularly optics."

Optics, natural philosophy—as science was called at that time, Barrow . . . Newton was beginning to digest the news and see grand possibilities. It might mean that he, Newton, would now have an opportunity to experiment. During the time he had been at Cambridge, the young man from Woolesthorpe had felt keenly the lack of an outlet for his highly developed manual dexterity. No one at Trinity seemed to care about science; the main interest there was still philosophy and theology. It all boiled down to endless discussions of finer and finer points, he used to say to himself.

Optics called for light experiments, the grinding of lenses, the construction of ingenious scientific apparatus. Newton's deft fingers were itching to get started. But first he must again go through his copy of Kepler's *Optics*. Difficult reading! But he simply had to master that book during the next few weeks or Barrow's lectures might prove too difficult to follow.

"What do you think of all this information I've just poured into your ears?" asked Wickins gaily, as he watched a slow glow spread over his friend's usually immobile face.

"I think the news is good—even grand!" answered Newton with a faraway look.

"And don't you feel that it calls for a little celebration?" continued Wickins with a wink.

Isaac Newton thought hard for a few seconds. "I certainly think it does!"

With that, the two young men walked out, arm in arm, and made for their favorite tavern to celebrate the great academic event.

Isaac Barrow, shortly after his appointment as Lucasian professor, was only twelve years older than the young man whose studies he was to oversee and whose career he was to influence so profoundly. The reputation of Barrow had already reached fabulous proportions in academic circles. As a youngster, he had proven restless, precocious and hard to control, but there was a marked improvement when Isaac Barrow grew to manhood. He was educated at Trinity College and became a Fellow in 1649. After six years as a Fellow, he was driven from England by the Puritans because of his outspoken opposition to their political and religious ideas. The next four years saw the exiled Barrow wandering through eastern Europe, where he managed to survive attacks by pirates and highwaymen during a series of almost unbelievable adventures.

In 1659, when conditions at home had become safer for one with his views, Barrow returned to England. Shortly afterward he was ordained to the ministry and appointed professor of Greek at Cambridge. From there the restless Barrow moved on to Gresham College, in London, where he became professor of mathematics; and a year later, he was back at Cambridge as the first Lucasian professor of mathematics.

The teacher who was destined to play so important a role in Newton's intellectual development was drawn to the quiet, thoughtful country youth from their very first meeting. The lean, slovenly dressed Barrow, whose caustic wit and unusual courage had made him a favorite of Charles II, was gentle and fatherly in his relation with Newton.

He liked the young scholar's intensity and intellectual vigor; he was thrilled to find a student who loved mathematics and science for their own sakes, and whose keen mind could quietly get to the heart of almost any subject he tackled. And there was no desire for fame, no ambition to shine in the academic world, Barrow noted approvingly. The unworldly Newton was a gem, and a rare one at that, decided the older man.

"Lincolnshire has sent us someone blessedly different in the person of Newton," he said to Dr. Babbington, a Trinity Fellow distantly related to Mr. Clark, the Grantham apothecary, and hence interested in the youth from Woolesthorpe. "God has planted an unusually productive mind in this young man.

It is our duty to clear the stones from around it so that the plant may grow tall and strong."

Influenced by the teacher whom he loved and admired, Isaac Newton was soon reading works by Wallis and Descartes—two of the most advanced mathematicians of the time. In addition, he became absorbed in experiments which required the grinding of lenses—an undertaking Newton regarded as a form of relaxation. It was during this very period that his mind began to grapple with the refraction of light as well as with certain mathematical problems which were to lead to his famous binomial theorem!

From the very beginning, when he had gotten a glimpse of the young man's natural mathematical ability, Dr. Barrow had cautioned Newton not to neglect Euclid.

"Why haven't you spent more time on Euclidean geometry?" he demanded sternly of Newton one day.

The young man flushed. "I read Euclid through hastily a few years ago, sir, but it seemed so self-evident that I didn't spend much time on it," confessed Newton.

"Self-evident?" repeated Barrow dryly. "Don't underestimate Euclid, Mr. Newton. His geometry furnishes us with a wonderful scientific tool which few know how to use effectively."

In 1664, three years after he had entered Trinity, Newton was elected to a scholarship. On this occasion Barrow, who was one of the examiners, again took the opportunity to stress the importance of Euclid to his favorite pupil.

"You should have seen Newton's face," laughed Barrow when he related the incident to Babbington. "It turned beet-red. I wanted to strike hard because that reticent youth will soon be so far ahead of us that we won't be able to reach him to strike." The admirer of the great Euclid thought for a moment, then added, "Our young friend is going to have a firm foundation to his mathematics—if I can manage it!"

Years later, Isaac Newton wrote that his great mistake, during his undergraduate years, was in attacking the newer geometry of Descartes *before* he had achieved a thorough mastery of Euclid.

And this admission from a man who later became one of the great masters in the use of Euclidian geometry!

7

THE PLAGUE YEARS

In January, 1665, Isaac Newton took his degree of Bachelor of Arts, along with twenty-five other Trinity men. By this time there was no question in his mind but that he would continue his studies in the academic atmosphere he had learned to love. Barrow had intimated to the young man, with whose growing intellectual power he was becoming more and more impressed, that there was an excellent possibility of the latter's obtaining a coveted Fellowship at Trinity.

Newton was thrilled at the idea of becoming a Fellow. For one thing this position carried with it an income which would free him almost entirely from money worries; also—and this was most important to the young scholar—a Fellow enjoyed complete freedom to occupy himself as he pleased with study, meditation or experiment.

This last consideration loomed large in the eyes of Newton. There was so much he wanted to do! His mind was astir with fresh ideas in this springtime of his intellectual life. Like rich black soil, freshly turned, his brain teemed with productiveness. . . .

There was the binomial theorem—he had that to work out; and the telescope improvement, for which he had already begun to fashion parts—there was that to do. And then there was the glass prism which formed the rainbow colors in a manner suggesting a long list of unanswerable questions. Finally, he planned to devote considerable time to the why's of Kepler's laws. Why did the planets move as they did? There were interesting calculations involved and he was looking forward to performing them.

The reserved country youth kept his thoughts strictly to himself. He was now a B.A., after three and a half years at Trinity. There would be lots of time later in which to carry out his projects; right now was a good time to relax. So Isaac Newton proceeded to celebrate the occasion by several visits to a tavern, by playing cards—and losing—and by buying gifts for Anne and oranges for the children at Woolesthorpe.

In the midst of the few pleasant weeks of release from studies, the ever-alert Wickins arrived with alarming news.

"They may close the College for an indefinite time," he announced. "That's the rumor, at any rate. The plague seems to be moving north out of London—according to the last report."

"That means we'll probably have to scatter until the plague subsides," observed Newton.

"Exactly. They won't want to expose the students here to that horrible danger. The plague may never get to Cambridge, but the authorities can't afford to risk it."

It was true that the Black Death was again on the march! The summer of 1664 had been dry and hot in London; the city had suffered from a plague of flies, ants and other insects. In the following year came the terrible Great Plague in which London lost one fifth of its population!

What served to make the attack of the bubonic plague even more terrifying was the fact that there had been a thirty-year period of immunity from the disease. People had assured themselves that with the increased comforts and security of the times, there would be no further attacks of the dreaded plague. Since the fourteenth century, the Black Death had continued to break out in England at odd times and in different localities—mainly towns and ports where the flea-bearing rat found it easy to multiply.

As it turned out, the year Newton was at Cambridge, 1665, was the last time the bubonic plague was to terrify England.

The officials at Cambridge watched the progress of the Great Plague anxiously. Deaths were mounting in London; it was becoming impossible even to find enough able-bodied men to bury the dead. Soon the disease appeared in East Anglia, but it was not yet spreading north or west—although isolated cases had been reported in those areas.

Finally on August 8, 1665, came the decision to close the University. To wait any longer would be foolhardy. The students were ordered to disperse.

"Are you going to be home for a long time?" asked his mother when Newton arrived unexpectedly at Woolesthorpe even before the University had been officially shut down.

"I don't know," smiled her son, looking far from upset at the prospect at living at home for a long period. "It depends on whether or not the plague weakens. It might be a few months or even longer."

"I'm so glad you didn't stay in Cambridge," observed his mother with relief. She looked around at the grass and trees. "There's no healthier place than Woolesthorpe. We have good air here and good food. The plague will never get to us," she added confidently.

That night, after the children had gone to bed, mother and son sat up for a long time, for they found quiet pleasure in each other's company. The widow wanted to know what Dr. Barrow had said to Isaac about the Fellowship. Her Isaac a Fellow of Trinity College! She beamed at the very prospect! Her brother, the Rector, had already given her an inkling of the desirability of that position, and of how few could hope to be elected to it.

"And Dr. Barrow felt that you might be made a Fellow?" pursued Hannah Smith.

Her son smiled. "Not immediately, Mother. All Dr. Barrow said was that it was in the offing, and that he, personally, would do his best to get a Fellowship for me."

The widow looked at her son proudly. "He must think well of you, Isaac."

"Perhaps he does. He and I get along very nicely. By the way, do you know that Barrow is never without his pipe? They say he smoked it even at the Court, and that the King did not object."

"It's such a dirty habit," cried his mother. "The odor of tobacco penetrates one's clothing—and in time even one's flesh!"

"Yes, it is pretty strong stuff," agreed her son, not revealing that he, too, had recently been experimenting with a pipe.

Suddenly Hannah Smith looked disturbed. "What if the College remains closed for several months—or even a year?"

Isaac appeared quite calm at the prospect. "I have brought considerable work with me from Cambridge—plenty of it. There are several matters I expect to look into while I am here. But I'll have time to help you with farm work, Mother," he assured her.

The widow laughed. "No you won't! Things are going smoothly now and I don't want them disturbed. You stick to your studies, Isaac, and the farm will take care of itself."

So Isaac Newton got himself settled in the closetlike room on the second floor of the manor house. As it turned out, the vacation lengthened into two years of intermittent "leisure"—a strange word for the most creative and exciting period in Newton's life! "In those days," he wrote many years later, referring to the plague years, "I was in the prime of my age for invention, and minded mathematics and philosophy more than at any time since."

At this period he began to puzzle over the moon's motions, a problem which was to intrigue him for many years afterwards. While an undergraduate at Trinity in 1664, he had made several attempts to measure the halos of the moon. And as he examined the heavens on those crisp autumn nights in Lincolnshire, Newton recalled many unanswered questions about the earth's satellite.

What kept the moon moving so smoothly and unhurriedly around the earth in an orbit which it completed every 27⅓ days? There above him was the shining quarter moon! The satellite's mysterious and effortless motion had fascinated human beings for thousands of years. Why did it behave as it did? The *how* was known but not the *why!*

About fifty years before Newton, Kepler had succeeded magnificently in describing the motions of planets by means of his famous laws of planetary motion. That great astronomer had guessed that the inverse square law was somehow involved, and that there was a definite gravitational attraction between the sun and the planets. But that was as far as Kepler and others could advance; and there the problem had long rested.

During the long days and evenings at Woolesthorpe, the

reflective twenty-four-year-old Bachelor of Arts pondered over many weighty questions. Refusing to be intimidated by the likelihood of failure, Newton insisted on coming to grips with problems which had long baffled the best minds of his own and previous generations.

Isaac Newton felt intuitively that there must be a gravitational force between the sun and the planets, and that the strength of this attractive force must decrease with the distance—also that the decrease wasn't merely proportional to the distance, but rather to the square of the distance. In other words, this was the famous inverse square law: twice as far away results in one fourth of the attractive force; three times as far, one ninth of the force; sixty times as far, one thirty-six hundredth of the force, and so on.

Again and again the young thinker scrutinized Kepler's Third Law, that mysterious statement which neither the discoverer nor anyone else seemed to find reasonable. "The squares of the times taken by the planets to travel around the sun vary as the cube of their mean distances from the sun"—stated the Third Law.

Like a hawk, the young man's mathematical mind kept hovering over this law, intent on finding a clue which would make it reasonable, logical. The puzzle—and Newton loved puzzles—was always with him: eating, sitting, walking or sleeping, it was always in his consciousness. Then came the moment when the intensity of his attack won him an answer! It came to Newton suddenly, as if out of the blue.

He made a few hurried calculations and emerged flushed and excited. There it was—at last. He had succeeded in deducing the inverse square law, mathematically, from Kepler's Third Law! What Kepler had suspected, this twenty-four-year-old youth had managed to prove by an amazing exhibition of mathematical insight.

Days and weeks passed during which Newton occupied himself with other problems, equally stimulating and satisfying. There was nothing like change, he would say to himself, for keeping a keen edge on one's mind.

"You're not eating well, Isaac," his mother would complain when she saw the food which had been brought to his room early in the day still untouched hours later. "And you can't possibly get enough sleep when you study far into the morning."

Her son listened absently and, as usual, promised that he would eat regularly and sleep the normal number of hours—in the future.

On sunny afternoons, Newton liked to sit in the shade of a favorite apple tree in the orchard not far from the manor house. There he would relax physically while his mind wrestled with exciting questions about light, the solar system and methods of calculating the areas of curves. . . .

One day, while thinking of other things, an apple fell from the tree under which he was sitting and landed at his feet. Instantly Newton's alert mind seized upon this everyday occurrence. That apples fall to the earth was nothing new; men had been aware of gravitation from ancient times. And Galileo, who died the year Newton was born, had discovered exactly how a freely falling body, like an apple, behaves.

But Newton's soaring mind did not stick to the apple; it immediately shifted from apple to moon. The attractive force of the earth extended to the top of the tree; that explained why apples fall to the ground. Did this same attractive force exert a pull on a body a hundred times as far away as the top of the tree? A thousand times as far away? What would the force of attraction amount to—at the distance of the moon? And finally, does the earth attract the moon as it does an apple?

Many questions and no answers! If the earth's gravitational pull extends as far as the moon, then why doesn't the moon fall to the earth like the apple?

For a long time the absorbed Newton could find no satisfactory answer to the last question. But awake or asleep, he kept driving his mind to produce an explanation, all the while waiting tensely for that glorious moment of illumination which would repay him amply for his labors. At last it came to him! It was all so simple. The answer was that the moon was actually falling toward the earth every moment—yes, actually falling while still maintaining the same distance from our planet!

Newton could see it all now—the simple concept which had escaped Galileo and others. The moon was like a projectile which was moving so fast that it fell as the horizon fell. In short, the moon's fall followed the curvature of the earth. If it were not dropping toward the earth every instant, then the moon's velocity would carry it off into space in a straight line, like mud thrown from a rapidly rotating wheel. The fact that the satellite kept moving round and round our planet proved that it was continually falling toward the latter.

His next task was to try to calculate how far an object would fall in one second, due to the pull of the earth, if the object were as far away from us as the moon. The distance of the moon's center from the earth's center is about sixty times the radius of the earth. If the inverse square law holds true, argued Newton, the attractive force of the earth on the moon must be $1/60 \times 60$ or $1/3600$ of what it is on the earth's surface.

An apple falls sixteen feet in the first second after being dropped, reflected Newton. If the apple were where the moon is, the former would fall $16/3600$ feet in one second. He now had the figure for how far the moon fell in one second!

How did this compare with the true figure for the moon's

fall in a second? Eagerly Newton began this crucial calculation. The distance of the moon from the earth was known; with this as his radius, it was easy to calculate the length of the giant circle which the moon followed around the earth. Knowing that it takes $27\frac{1}{3}$ days for the moon to go around this circle once, he was able to determine how many feet per second the moon moves in its orbit. Finally, using the figures he had just obtained, Newton drew a scale diagram and found exactly how much the moon falls off from the horizontal in one second, i.e., how many feet it drops toward the earth in a given time.

His theory required an answer of $^{16}/_{3600}$ feet in a second, as explained previously. However, the scale diagram gave him only $^{14}/_{3600}$ feet per second for the fall of the moon. Close enough, said Newton to himself. After all, his calculations were based on a rough figure for the radius of the earth—one later found to be inaccurate. At the time, however, he was too thrilled to worry over his results being slightly off. He kept his computations locked up in his notebook, not revealing their existence to anyone until sixteen years later—when a recalculation based on more accurate measurements of the size of the earth gave him an almost perfect result.

At Woolesthorpe, in 1665, Isaac Newton had no inkling that he had discovered the law of universal gravitation. True he was pleased with what he had accomplished; but to him it was only a beginning, for there were still basic questions to answer before his discovery could amount to anything important. What justification did he have, for example, for treating the moon as if it were an apple, a mere point in the sky? He had disregarded the real size of the moon in his calculations. This made the whole matter more or less something of a guess. And until he could present a thorough, foolproof case for his theory, it must remain what it was—a hunch, a mere possibility.

Newton now turned, for relief, to the activity he enjoyed most—experimental investigation. His experiments at Cambridge with a triangular glass prism had convinced him, despite prevailing opinion, that white light was not homogeneous, that it was not all of one kind. How could it be, when passage through a glass prism made it emerge as a band of rainbow colors? He had also discovered that the different colors in white light, on passing through the glass prism, were not bent or refracted equally: the red was bent least and the violet most!

He repeated earlier experiments in his little room at Woolesthorpe, using simple homemade equipment. A darkened room . . . a round hole in a window shutter . . . a triangular glass prism . . . a beam of sunlight. And there on the screen opposite the shutter was the beautiful spectrum of white light—with all the colors of the rainbow! He noticed that the band of color was larger than the hole in the shutter; and also, that the band was five times longer than it was wide.

Newton was unable to explain the shape of the band. He tried combining two prisms, one in a reversed position. Now he got no colored band at all, but only a spot of sunlight. It was mystifying, for the young man was working in an uncharted field. He tried isolating one of the colors in the spectrum by passing it through a second prism.

His head was spinning. No books had ever mentioned the phenomena he had just observed. It would take a vast amount of experimental work and a great deal of thinking before he could hope to arrive at an adequate explanation of what he had seen happen. Newton didn't realize that he was laying the foundations of spectrum analysis, which was later to play so important a role in modern physics, chemistry and astronomy.

Always unhurried when it came to publishing his findings, Newton felt that all of his exciting work at Woolesthorpe was only a beginning. His original ideas on gravity, light and the calculus were each destined to take ten years to bring to fruition. At the moment he saw no need to rush into print; a few pages of notes, for his own use, would suffice. . . .

The third subject to draw Newton's attention during his enforced vacation was of a purely mathematical nature. Only a few months before the plague broke out, his fertile brain had discovered the binomial theorem, which in its simpler form is now part of the high school algebra course. This accomplishment alone, in the opinion of scholars, would have assured Newton an honored place in the history of mathematics.

At Woolesthorpe, however, his mind kept pushing ahead, as if with a momentum which its owner could not control. Some hints in books by John Wallis, a prominent Oxford mathematician, plus illuminating lectures by Barrow, led Newton to seek a new way of calculating the areas of curves. It was a difficult problem. How does one find out how many square inches there are in a piece of a circle or ellipse, for example?

The greatest of the Greek mathematicians had attempted to solve this type of problem—but failed. Isaac Newton, at the age of twenty-four, decided to sink his teeth into it, using all the available knowledge of his time. He had a hunch about a new method, a different approach entirely. He tried it—and it worked! In 1666, he calculated the area of a hyperbola "to two-and-fifty figures by the same method"!

With unbelievable energy, Newton moved ahead swiftly from his binomial theorem to lay the foundations of his method of fluxions. The latter developed into the differential and integral calculus, the key tools of modern science as well as the cornerstone of the mathematics of today.

Newton regarded his accomplishments as important to himself only. Since personal curiosity rather than a desire for fame had motivated him, the young thinker saw no reason why the outside world should be at all interested. It was an extraordinary attitude toward one's achievements, but Newton maintained it stubbornly throughout his lifetime. In a way, Isaac Newton was like a man who sets for himself difficult tasks, which he then compels himself to perform perfectly. And that was all there was to it, as far as the performer was concerned!

Alas! Anne Storey never could understand the change in her suitor's attitude during the two years of his "vacationing" at his mother's farm. His visits to Grantham became less and less frequent; and when he did call on his friend, the results were exceedingly unsatisfactory to the warmhearted, gay young lady.

"He's so different," she used to complain to her mother. "Isaac is not the same person he was when he lived with us—or even last year."

"What do you mean?" asked Mrs. Clark.

"I don't know—it's the way he looks at me. It's so strange. I feel that he's thinking of something else all the time he's with me. He makes me think—I—I hardly exist—almost as if I were part of the room or the furniture. And yet he doesn't want to hurt me, I know he doesn't."

"Isaac is a scholar now, Anne," said her mother gently, "and an unusually original one, from what I hear."

"But why—why doesn't he look at me the way he used to?" cried the unhappy girl.

Mrs. Clark put her arm around her daughter. "It isn't you, dear. Isaac doesn't think of himself, he doesn't think of you, he doesn't think of me. His mind is full of his studies. He never thinks of people, but only of ideas. Hannah Smith tells me he is set on remaining at Trinity as a Fellow."

"I could sense that," murmured Anne, trying to hold back her tears. "He wants to be a scholar . . . he wants to be a scholar . . . all his life!"

There was no discussion, but by mutual consent the engagement was broken off. Anne Storey was too pretty to remain unattached for very long. Soon after the break with the idea-intoxicated, uncommunicative Isaac, she married a local youth.

But for the rest of his long life, Isaac Newton never forgot the girl from Grantham; he always made it a point to inquire about her well-being and insisted on helping her financially whenever she was in need—which, unfortunately, was often.

Anne, a widow in her old age after having married twice, always spoke affectionately of the famous man who had been her dear companion in his youth. She used to try to imagine what life would have been like—if their plans had remained unchanged and they had married. . . .

8

THE REFLECTING TELESCOPE

By the spring of 1667, the plague had definitely subsided after taking the lives of one-fifth of the population of London.

Newton had a pleasant feeling of accomplishment as he looked back at the two years of "leisure" on the farm. And why not? In the entire history of science we find nothing to equal the extraordinary creativeness of his mind—during so brief a period of time!

Now that he knew his brain was fertile and that it could be forced to produce, Newton looked forward eagerly to the years ahead. Time and problems were all he needed; and if things went well, he would enjoy an abundance of both for the rest of his life. He was not afraid of work; he felt confident that he could drive his mind to do anything he wanted it to do. No brain was ever less pampered than Newton's!

But a life of pure ideas wasn't enough. Change was important because it rested mind and body. He was therefore anxious to return to his telescope project—abandoned during the plague years—and get down to the business of grinding lenses and fashioning metal parts. Also, there were those puzzling experiments on light and color to repeat and explain; and finally, he promised himself the greatest treat of all someday soon—the outfitting of a complete chemical laboratory in the garden in back of his room. . . .

"What a sad waste of time the plague caused us!" exclaimed Dr. Barrow when Newton called to pay his respects. "And just when you were making excellent progress in mathematics, Mr. Newton." He paused for a moment as he eyed his undemonstrative pupil. "Did you keep up with your studies while at Woolesthorpe?" he asked with a smile.

"Yes," said Newton. "I did a little work."

"I know," snorted Barrow. "You were probably occupied with the plow or the scythe."

The young man smiled. "My mother refused to allow me to apply my talents to farming, sir. She said the farm always ran better without my help."

Barrow nodded understandingly. "Sons are often trials to parents—too often. I know I was. Young people are apt to be headstrong, self-absorbed and thoughtless. I myself was a perfect example of unmanageable youth in my day." He looked aside for a few seconds as he recalled certain painful incidents of his own childhood and youth.

"By the way, Mr. Newton," the older man called out as his pupil was about to leave, "have you done anything with that infinite series idea you mentioned to me just before we shut down?"

"Yes, sir," admitted the modest Newton, "I did a bit of work on it. I tried to develop the method in some detail. In fact, I am planning a short paper on it."

"A paper? Good! I'll look forward to reading it."

"There are a few points I still have to clear up in my mind,

Dr. Barrow. I wonder—if—if you could find the time to read and criticize the paper when it is finished?"

"I'll be happy to do that," his teacher assured the young man.

Spurred on by Barrow's interest, Newton spent the first few months after his return to Trinity in the preparation of his mathematical paper. This contribution, entitled *On Analysis of Equations with an infinite number of terms,* was in the opinion of later scholars a mature and carefully organized piece of work.

When Barrow was presented with the manuscript by the shy, unassuming Newton, the former ran his eyes over it quickly, looking more and more startled as he read on. It was difficult reading, he said to himself, and so different—and new! He stole a quick, curious glance at the quiet young scholar. Had the latter strayed from the path somewhere—or was he a person of unusual originality?

"I'll have to study it carefully before venturing an opinion," Barrow finally declared. "At any rate, please accept my congratulations, Mr. Newton, for having used your long period of leisure to such great advantage."

Newton thanked his professor and departed. The young man felt relieved now that the mathematical portion of his researches was in another's hands. The paper was no longer of any concern to him. Newton was planning to throw his energies into the telescope project—and what prospect could be more attractive?

In 1667, six months after Trinity had reopened, Newton was elected a Minor Fellow, and not long after that he was admitted as Major Fellow. The young scholar was overjoyed; the examinations had been difficult and he had not been too optimistic about his success. Now he could scarcely wait for the end of the year to get back to Woolesthorpe. He was anxious to share his good fortune with his family.

At last the winter vacation drew around and Newton boarded the slow coach for home. The journey seemed interminable to the impatient Fellow; the narrow roads were piled high with snow, and it was difficult to see where road ended and unenclosed heath and fen began. Twice the coach got stuck in heavy drifts from which it had to be pulled out by teams of oxen furnished by neighboring farmers.

"So my Isaac is now a Fellow of Trinity College," cried his mother proudly the moment she saw him.

Soon his whole family was bustling about the first Fellow in the memory of the Newton family, and throwing question after question at the amused Isaac.

"Perhaps my good fortune was due to an accident—or accidents," he remarked with a twinkle.

"We don't believe that!" answered his excited and loyal audience—almost in unison.

"It happened," began Isaac slowly, "that there were nine vacancies to be filled—an unusually large number. You see, there had been no elections to the Fellowships for two years because of the plague." He paused for a few seconds, then added with a faint smile, "Two of the vacancies were caused by Fellows falling down staircases."

There was loud laughter at this explanation.

Hannah Smith suddenly looked concerned. "Are the staircases at Trinity so dangerous, Isaac?"

"I never found them so, Mother," he answered seriously. "They're safe enough—if one remembers how to walk."

The young people got the full significance of Isaac's remark even though his mother didn't. Isaac felt it wiser not to explain that drunkenness among Trinity Fellows was not uncommon during the period of his residence.

As always, Newton found the atmosphere at Woolesthorpe relaxing and heartwarming. Once he found himself in the bosom of his family, the reserve and shyness which characterized his attitude toward strangers disappeared quickly.

Alone with his mother that first evening, Isaac told her what he felt would please her most about his promotion.

"I'll have an income as Fellow which often is as high as one hundred pounds a year, Mother. I won't have to ask you for help from now on. Perhaps—I'll even be able to help you."

Hannah Smith looked impressed. Not only was her son an honored Fellow, but he was also going to be paid for being one!

"I'll not need your help, Isaac. Use the money to buy things for your work. Don't worry about the farm. Things here are going much more smoothly than they did a few years ago. Conditions have improved—and the children are now beginning to take care of themselves."

"Are you sure?" asked Isaac anxiously. He could use his income from the Fellowship to purchase materials he had long wanted—parts for his telescope, chemical apparatus and books.

His mother nodded firmly. "I am sure, Isaac. I want you to keep that hundred pounds a year for yourself, so let us not discuss it any further."

During those few pleasant weeks at home, Isaac Newton for once permitted himself the luxury of real idleness. He spent considerable time with the children; and when Benjamin, who was now almost sixteen years old, asked what he was going to work on as a Fellow, Newton casually mentioned the telescope.

"A telescope!" cried the boy, all excited. "I know what that is—something one looks through to see the moon and faraway stars. How do you make a telescope?"

Newton was a little surprised at the boy's excitement. During the plague years he had never tried to explain to his family what he was engaged in, because the ideas themselves were too difficult. True, he had allowed the children to play with the glass prisms; and he remembered how thrilled they were when the brightly colored spectrum appeared on the kitchen wall. At that time Isaac hadn't even attempted to explain the colors except in a matter-of-fact way, for it was obvious that the theory of color was too much for the youngsters.

But now that Benjamin was really interested, Isaac decided it would be fun to explain telescopes to the young people.

Before long, all three—Benjamin, Hannah, and Mary—were sitting at the feet of the Trinity Fellow listening open-mouthed to what he was saying about lenses and telescopes.

Isaac told his fascinated audience of Hans Lippershey, the Dutch spectacle-maker, who in 1609 happened to hold up two lenses and glance through them. It was a bright day. The distance between the concave and convex lens was just right and the concave was the one close to his eye. Lippershey was amazed at being able to see a distant church steeple clearly; it seemed as large, through the lenses, as if he were seeing it from close by. The Dutchman had discovered the first telescope!

"And no one had ever thought of looking through two such lenses before?" asked Benjamin incredulously.

"No," answered Isaac with a smile. "People don't like to try new things."

The home instructor went on to tell of Galileo who, on hearing of Lippershey's discovery, immediately began to build a telescope of his own. The great Italian scientist was not satisfied with the magnification of three or four diameters offered by the early instruments. Soon he was grinding lenses to a curvature based on his own calculations. After painstaking work, he finally succeeded in building a telescope with a magnification of thirty diameters! The combination of lenses used by Galileo was still the same: concave for the eyepiece, convex for the objective.

"And what did Galileo see when he looked through his grand telescope?" asked Hannah, showing a keen sense of the practical.

"Galileo saw in the heavens things which no man had ever seen before," explained Isaac. "He discovered that the moon was not round and smooth but rather rough and pitted. The Milky Way, said Galileo, consisted of a vast number of distant stars. And most important of all, he was the first man ever to observe the four moons circling the planet Jupiter —not one moon such as the earth has, but four!"

"Four moons!" sighed the group in amazement.

"And was Galileo's telescope the best ever made—the best there is now?" asked Mary.

Isaac was enjoying the rapt expressions on the faces around him. "It was the best," he continued, "until Kepler came along and showed that it was better to use two convex lenses rather than a concave-convex combination. And Kepler was right: his system gave a wider and clearer field."

"So that's the best telescope, then," concluded Benjamin.

At this point, the teacher had the feeling that he was about to lose the attention of his young listeners. How could he explain to them that Kepler's system brought with it difficulties not encountered in the earlier telescopes? If a convex lens is spherical, then the part near the edges, where the glass is curved most, will bend the emerging light rays most sharply. On the other hand, the rays passing through the center where the lens is curved least, will emerge with relatively slight bending. The unfortunate result of such differences in bending angle is the formation of an indistinct image; in the language of science, the lenses produced "spherical aberration."

The renowned French scientist Descartes had investigated this problem in 1637, and recommended two possible solutions. The first was that lenses be ground to elliptical rather than spherical shape—something the lens grinders of the time were incapable of doing. The second was to utilize convex lenses of slight curvature, even if that required the construction of long, clumsy telescopes.

After one or two attempts to go more deeply into the history of telescopes, Isaac gave up. Instead he brought down several lenses, and soon the entire family was marveling at the sharp image of a near-by tree formed on a sheet of paper by a large convex lens.

Suddenly Benjamin, who was peering through a thick lens, cried out, "I see colors, I see rainbow colors!"

"You do," agreed Isaac. "And that's still another fault of the Kepler telescope. Even if the convex lenses are ground to only a slight curvature, and the telescope tubes made ridiculously long, there will still be the nuisance of the color fringe. We call this 'chromatic aberration.' It unfortunately adds to the indistinctness of the image."

"Can't anything be done about that trouble?" asked Mary.

"No—not as yet. The different colors in white light are bent to different degrees as they pass through the lens. The red is bent least and the violet most."

Very modestly, Isaac Newton did not reveal that, of all scientists of the time, only he was aware of the true cause of the color fringe around images! Even the great Descartes could not offer an acceptable explanation of chromatic aberration. Newton had hit upon the real reason for the color fringe as the result of the experiments he had performed with the glass prism; the spectrum of white light give him the long-sought explanation.

"And when you build your telescope—what kind will it be,

Isaac?" asked Benjamin, looking proudly at his erudite half brother.

Isaac did not answer immediately. He was searching for an elementary explanation of his telescope improvement.

"I'm going to make a tube which will be fairly short and have a concave mirror at the bottom of it—not a lens, but a mirror. This curved mirror will form an image in the air inside the tube."

"But how will you be able to see the image?" persisted Benjamin. "You'll have to stick your head into the tube. Even if it were very wide, your head would get in the way, wouldn't it?"

Isaac laughed. "We can get around that. I'm planning to bore a hole in the side of the tube and peek in from the outside. A very small mirror inside the tube will reflect the image to the observer outside."

He paused for a moment. "I don't know if it will work—but I'm going to try. What I must get, first of all, is the right kind of metal for my large curved mirror. I'll have to polish and polish this mirror until it becomes a perfect concave reflector."

"Are you going to build it here?" asked Hannah eagerly. "I'd love to look through a telescope and see all the moons around Jupiter!"

Isaac shook his head. "No, I haven't collected all my equipment yet, and it will take me a while to put the telescope together." He noted the open disappointment on the faces around him and quickly added, "But we can build a simple Galilean telescope right here. I have the lenses—and all we have to do is to mount them in a long tube. It won't be perfect, but I know you'll all enjoy looking through it."

There were outcries of enthusiasm at his offer; and soon Isaac Newton was busily engaged in fashioning a little telescope for his family to look through and thrill over.

Those were happy, relaxed weeks for the young man. Christmas of 1667 came and went, but the Trinity Fellow lingered at Woolesthorpe. He was reluctant to leave even though he was looking forward to the year ahead. Home was so pleasant. . . .

9

LUCASIAN PROFESSOR

When Newton got back to Cambridge, late in January of 1668, he found Barrow anxiously awaiting his arrival. The latter was sitting at his desk, smoking his pipe and deep in thought, when the young man called. In his teacher's hands was the mathematical paper Newton had submitted a few months before.

"So here you are at last!" exclaimed Barrow.

"I stayed on at Woolesthorpe longer than I had expected," apologized Newton. "Christmas in the country makes one lazy. I enjoyed it so much I found it hard to leave the farm."

"Very sensible," said the older man approvingly. "I have your paper here, Mr. Newton. After I had studied it carefully, I asked a few friends to read it—hoping you would not mind. The method you describe is so original that I felt the opinions of outsiders would be worth-while."

There was a heavy stillness in the room when Barrow paused to relight his pipe. Newton kept shifting in his chair, looking nervous and embarrassed. So the first fruit of his teeming brain had been exposed to the eyes of the world! To get an idea and develop it for one's self was a satisfying experience. But to get an idea and then have to worry about what people would say about it—that was something else again!

"It's ingenious, it's original, it's vastly useful," said Barrow suddenly. "You've taken an important step forward, a step in a new direction. I'm proud of you, Mr. Newton. A magnificent performance!"

The young man flushed. "I merely took some hints from you and from Wallis and put them together to form my new method, Dr. Barrow."

His teacher let out a roar of laughter. "It wasn't as easy as that, Mr. Newton. The point is that I didn't think of it, Wallis didn't think of it—but you did. And a masterly presentation this is!" he cried, flourishing the paper.

"Have you tested your method of computing the areas of curves? I mean have you applied it to any practical problem?" Barrow asked curiously.

"Yes, sir," answered Newton quietly. "While in Lincolnshire during the plague, I computed the area of a hyperbola to two-and-fifty figures by the same method."

"Wonderful!" exclaimed Barrow. "Will you let me send your paper to John Collins in London? He must see it, he must!"

Newton seemed puzzled by the request.

"I must tell you about Collins," smiled Barrow. "He is a gentle soul, a lovable and generous man, a self-taught mathematician. Collins acts as a sort of clearing house for ideas—a human scientific journal. If he finds your paper as exciting as I do, Collins will copy and circulate it among the most important mathematicians of the world. He does it all at his own expense—poor though he is—and only because he loves science and mathematics."

Newton's face had reddened. "I wouldn't mind at all, Dr. Barrow, if he read it. But—but I prefer that my name not be attached to the paper."

Barrow was both startled and amused. "Anonymous? You're a modest young man, Mr. Newton! However, if you insist, I'll ask Mr. Collins to follow your wishes in this matter. Still, Mr. Newton, you must think of yourself, and of moving ahead in the academic world. Your name on a paper of such merit as this will certainly not harm you."

"I'd feel better if my name were not on the paper," repeated Newton nervously.

"As you say," said Barrow genially. "But I wish you'd think about the matter, anyway," he added as the young man was about to leave.

This incident reveals the part of Newton's character which his own and later generations found so baffling, so hard to understand. Newton actually attached little importance to his own accomplishments in physics and mathematics, the very fields in which he excelled. In almost every case, valuable papers of startling originality had to be pried from him by tactful friends.

Once he had experienced the glow, the creative glow, resulting from the successful completion of a task he had stubbornly set for himself, Newton was through! His notes would be thrown into some drawer to gather dust for years—until the insistence of friends would bring them to light.

Had the restless spotlight of public esteem never paused to illuminate the accomplishments of the silent, sober-browed, Lincolnshire genius, he would have remained fully content with his lot. "For I do not see what is desirable in public esteem," he wrote in 1669, "were I able to acquire and maintain it: it would perhaps increase my acquaintance, the thing which I chiefly study to decline."

It is unjust to criticize Newton for not being a well-rounded individual. For if he had possessed all the charming, agreeable qualities we expect in our great men, Newton would not have been the magnificent human being whose unsurpassed creativeness has for generations placed humanity in his debt. Since Newton's character is fascinating because it is so different, one should not be critical of the very differences which made it what it was.

On July 7, 1668, he was created Master of Arts. Newton was pleased because it meant that the way to academic advancement was now clear—if and when the opportunity came. Life at Cambridge was perfectly suited to one of his temperament. His sturdy body could stand the physical strain which resulted from his lifelong habit of applying himself, with superhuman intensity, to the pursuit of an idea. Newton wanted no more from life than the privilege of living out his years in the cloistered atmosphere of Trinity, surrounded by books and laboratory equipment.

The next few months were crowded with work for him. Barrow, about to publish his lectures on optics and geometry, had entrusted his gifted pupil with the task of preparing the manuscript for the printer. In the fall, Newton journeyed to London to purchase the equipment he needed for the optical experiments he had in mind, the telescope he was almost ready to build, the chemical laboratory he intended to lay out. This last project was perhaps closest to his heart; as it turned out it was in the field of chemistry that Newton, for the rest of his life, was to find the pleasure and relaxation his mind needed.

As soon as he returned to Cambridge with his purchases, he got busy on his telescope. Newton regarded this project as a recreation; it was going to give him the opportunity to work with his hands—something he had looked forward to for a long time.

With almost boyish eagerness he made his concave mirror by mixing copper and tin, and soon succeeded in giving it the high polish it required. The telescope turned out to be about one inch in diameter and six inches long. Inside the tube and close to where the image was formed by the concave mirror, Newton inserted a small plane mirror at an angle of forty-five degrees to the axis of the telescope. This mirror served to reflect the image to an external eyepiece through an opening in the *side* of the telescope tube.

It was Newton's idea that an external eyepiece would not only increase the magnification of his instrument but would also provide a comfortable observation point. Some years before, Gregory had published a plan for a reflecting telescope, but had never gotten around to constructing one. His idea was to cut a circular hole in the center of the mirror at the base of the telescope, and to look through this hole at the image formed inside the tube. Newton was of the opinion, however, that a small mirror placed inside the telescope tube would prove more efficient.

By means of his small reflecting telescope, the first of its kind, Newton was able to see the satellites of Jupiter and the horns of Venus. Short though it was, his instrument gave a magnification of forty. True, it was crude and small and did not have the correct curve for the reflecting mirror; looking back now, the mirror should have been parabolic, like the reflector of an automobile headlight, rather than spherical as Newton ground it.

Still, it was an all-important beginning; and soon the ingenious minds and skillful hands of other men were busy effecting improvements in Newton's little instrument. The giant reflecting telescopes of the great observatories of today can be traced back to the humble six-inch reflector built by Newton in his workroom at Trinity College.

Neither Newton nor his contemporaries were then aware that not all types of glass bend light rays to an equal degree i.e. possess the same refractive index. The former had jumped to the erroneous conclusion that chromatic aberration, which caused the annoying color fringes around images, could never be eliminated in telescopes based on refraction.

About seventy years later, Chester More Hall, a barrister in Essex, England, designed the first telescope free from color aberration. He took advantage of the fact, by then well known, that flint glass and crown glass have different refractive or bending powers; and he succeeded in combining the two types of glass so as to practically eliminate the color fringe difficulty. With this important improvement, the refracting telescopes took on a new lease on life, and soon were competing with reflecting telescopes for places in the great observatories of the world.

In the spring of the year 1669, while still in the midst of his telescope work, Newton was summoned by Barrow. Dropping everything, he hastened to the latter's chambers.

"Sit down, Mr. Newton," said the older man, rubbing his hands together gleefully. "I have good news for you."

Isaac found himself a chair and waited soberly for Barrow to begin.

"I've heard from John Collins at last," smiled the professor of mathematics. "He is as enthusiastic as I am about your paper and proposes to send copies to every important mathematician in England, Scotland, France, Italy, and Holland."

Barrow paused. "What do you think of that, sir?"

Newton was taken aback by the news. He was pleased, but at the same time somewhat unsteadied by what he had just heard. The young scholar was possessed by a strong sense of privacy, of reserve, of detachment. Now he would be much in the public eye, he reflected. Would he be able to think and work effectively if he were always conscious that other people were interested—and perhaps watching him critically?

"It is a great honor, Dr. Barrow," he finally managed to mumble.

"More than that," exclaimed the excitable Barrow, "it is a fine feather in the cap of English mathematics!" He became thoughtful for a few seconds. "Collins wants to know who wrote the paper. I confided that the author was recently created a Fellow at Trinity. But Collins isn't satisfied. He wants your name, Mr. Newton, he wants your name on that paper. Shall I send it to him?"

Newton felt cornered! What could he say that wouldn't sound childish? He didn't want publicity because of a vague fear that it might disturb his thinking. But would Barrow understand a reason like that? Probably not!

"What do you suggest, sir?" Newton murmured. "Do you think it necessary for my name to be on the paper? I'll go by your opinion, Dr. Barrow."

Barrow threw up his hands as if to indicate that any further discussion of the matter would be foolish. "Give him your name—of course! You've done an honest and valuable piece of work, Mr. Newton. There's no reason to hide your light under a bushel. Let Collins have it!"

"Very well, sir," said the younger man, but with reluctance. I'll be governed by your advice, Dr. Barrow."

"Good!" exclaimed Barrow, looking pleased. "And I'm sure you'll never regret it. It's the only sensible thing to do."

There was silence in the small room for several moments as the older man puffed away at his pipe. "I want you to become known to the world, Mr. Newton. Perhaps someday—not too far away—I may decide to relinquish the chair of mathematics in order to devote myself to studies much dearer to me. And if you, Mr. Newton, become widely known as a capable mathematician, perhaps—perhaps—you may even take my place here."

This last statement completely disorganized the younger man! What was Barrow saying? The Lucasian Chair of Mathematics for him, Isaac Newton? Successor to the great Barrow? Only a few years ago, he, Newton, had entered Trinity as a working student, a Sizar. It seemed only yesterday when he was congratulating himself at having been elected a Fellow. . . .

The sensitive Barrow managed to follow Newton's thoughts fairly closely—and was vastly amused. That Lincolnshire youth had something! he said to himself. Newton wasn't aware of it . . . Trinity wasn't aware of it . . . The world wasn't aware of it. But, he, Barrow, certainly was!

"Go now, Mr. Newton, and collect yourself," laughed the older man. "There's nothing assured about the future as there is nothing assured about anything in this world. Be that as it may, I still will venture to predict that someday England will be proud of you, Mr. Newton, very proud."

John Collins, the self-appointed liaison man for scientific ideas, did his work well. Before long every outstanding mathematician in England and on the Continent had been informed of Newton's unusual contribution. Even the great Leibnitz, one of the world's foremost mathematicians, expressed a desire to know more about the young Trinity Fellow's method of calculating the areas of curves. Collins took the opportunity to send Newton some problems on annuities whose solution had long baffled the experts in London. Newton solved them in short order, much to Collins' delight.

On October 29, 1669, Isaac Newton was appointed Lucasian Professor of Mathematics, largely due to the enthusiastic recommendation of Dr. Barrow, who was anxious to devote the remainder of his life to theological studies. The retiring professor managed to convince the Cambridge selection board that it was in the fortunate position of being able to find his successor in the person of the brilliant young man from Woolesthorpe.

And so Isaac Newton, at the age of twenty-seven, after eight years at Trinity, was elevated to one of the most famous chairs of mathematics in the world!

10

LIGHT TROUBLE

The Lucasian Professorship was perfectly suited to Isaac Newton's interests and temperament. It called for only one lecture a week during one term of the school year; in addition, the Lucasian professor was expected to confer with students twice weekly while in residence at Trinity College.

Newton was thus left with plenty of time for study and experiment. His salary as professor was one hundred pounds a year, which, added to the income he continued to receive as a Fellow, brought the total up to about two hundred pounds annually—a tidy sum in those days.

It was no simple matter for his students to follow his lectures on optics—Newton's first teaching subject. They saw a stocky man of medium height, with a high and somewhat receding forehead, prominent nose, square chin and brown eyes. Newton's manner lacked animation; he spoke slowly, as if he were thinking out loud rather than, like a teacher, repeating old thoughts. There was nothing theatrical or emotional about his delivery. Most of his students found the formidable lectures extremely difficult to digest, weighted as they were with so much solid substance.

Very often, not a single student would turn up for the

ordeal. Newton, far from upset, would wait the customary few minutes, then slowly walk back to his laboratory.

"Why don't you send your telescope to the Royal Society?" suggested his friend Wickins one day.

"It's only a crude model," exclaimed Newton. "Perhaps someday it will be sufficiently perfected to make it a valuable astronomical instrument." He never could understand why so many teachers and students at Cambridge were so interested in his reflecting telescope. To him it was a minor idea in which he had already lost interest.

Finally at the insistence of his colleagues, Newton decided to send the instrument to the Royal Society. By this time the original telescope had mysteriously disappeared, so its inventor had to go to the trouble of building another; and this second model was exhibited in London where it excited considerable comment. The members of the Society requested Newton to construct still another, which was shown to the public in 1671. The most important personages in England examined and looked through the instrument; even Charles II marveled at the little telescope which could perform as well as one several times longer.

Though it had been incorporated under a royal charter by Charles II as recently as 1662, the Royal Society for the Advancement of Learning was already an important cultural force in England. The members met regularly to discuss philosophy, science or any subject which interested them—except religion and politics, which were forbidden topics. As a reaction to the violence and bloodshed of the recent Civil War, science—or natural philosophy as it was then called—became the favorite study of educated men. Even the King dabbled in chemistry at that time.

The impression created by Newton's reflecting telescope was so favorable that the Bishop of Sarum proposed its inventor for membership. On January 11, 1672, Isaac Newton received his first public honor—election as Fellow of the Royal Society.

"It's hard for me to understand," Newton confided to Wickins, "why people insist on making such a fuss over my little telescope."

He was blissfully unaware at this time that Robert Hooke, the brilliant but vain curator of the Royal Society, had made some strange claims when the telescope was first exhibited in London. Hooke, who for many years was destined to play the role of an irritant in Newton's life, always looked at his fellow scientists with a jealous eye.

In the case of Newton's telescope, Hooke asserted that he himself had in the year 1664 "made a little tube of about an inch long to put on his fob, which performs more than any telescope of fifty feet after the common manner." And the only reason why Hooke had neglected to develop his pocket model was that he was too busy with other matters, and also—he did not want the London "glass grinders" to learn his secret! At that time, in 1672, Newton was extraordinarily innocent concerning the ways of men. For that matter, he retained a blind spot in regard to people for his entire life. This weakness, if it may be so called, was the other side of his genius: Newton found it absolutely necessary to forget both the world and himself when in pursuit of an idea. For weeks or even months, he would live in a trance-like state and think of nothing but the problem on whose solution his whole being was concentrated.

Most people learn about themselves and others from talking or reading about the thoughts and actions of various individuals. But Newton never experienced this type of self-education; he remained a solitary, uncommunicative thinker because of the nature of his mind and interests. To him ideas, and only ideas, were sharp and clear; people, on the other hand, were for him invariably poorly defined, blurred.

On his return to Cambridge, after a brief visit to Woolesthorpe, Newton wrote to Henry Oldenburg, the secretary of the Royal Society, expressing his appreciation of the honor which had been bestowed upon him. In this letter, the Cambridge professor hinted that there were a number of interesting ideas he would like to communicate to the Royal Society. Soon afterward, Newton wrote to Oldenburg again, saying he was planning to acquaint the society with the "philosophical discovery" which had led to the building of the reflecting telescope. This discovery Newton ventured to describe as "being in my judgment the oddest, if not the most considerable detection, which hath hitherto been made in the operations of nature."

For once in his life Isaac Newton was enthusiastic over one of his own achievements! He had never displayed any such feeling in regard to his law of gravitation or binomial theorem or telescope or differential calculus. But this was different! The fact that his light discoveries represented an experimental as well as intellectual triumph may have made them so much dearer to him. At any rate, so thrilled was Newton with his revolutionary work on light and color that he just could not keep his feet on the ground—but walked on air for a short time!

Even his roommate noticed that the usually serene Newton appeared somewhat on edge during the next few weeks. Wickins wondered if the honor of having been elected a Fellow of the Royal Society was responsible for his friend's suppressed excitement?

"Have you received any more reports on your telescope?" he asked one evening, as he watched Newton pacing the room.

"No, but I am about to send the Society a paper on light

and color. I've had the matter on my mind for a long time. It expresses views contrary to all the old ideas. I am sure it will be well received because of the experimental evidence."

Wickins was intrigued by the change in his friend. Gone was the faraway, indifferent attitude that had always characterized Newton. The young professor was glowing, nervous, excited!

"Will your paper describe the light experiments which you demonstrated before your students?"

"Yes, but this time my audience will consist of scientists and philosophers—men with keen minds. They will understand," added Newton confidently.

The Cambridge professor's communication to the Royal Society contained a complete account of his light experiments and theoretical conclusions. Upon receipt of the paper, entitled "The Composition of White Light," the Society immediately appointed a committee to consider it. Since the report brought in was distinctly favorable, the order was given to publish Newton's contribution in the *Philosophical Transactions*, the official organ of the Royal Society.

In his paper, Newton described in detail the series of experiments which had led him to conclude that white light is made up of several different colors . . . Each color is bent or refracted to a different degree when passed through a triangular glass prism . . . The least refracted are the colors at the red end of the spectrum, and the most refracted those at the violet end . . . Once a color has been separated from white light it could not itself be changed or broken up in any way . . . All the prism did was to separate the colors in white light . . . Finally, this separation or dispersion is the real cause of the brilliantly colored spectrum.

Newton's simple experiments were beautifully planned and executed; and his conclusions followed logically from the experimental evidence. Here at last was a down-to-earth, fact-supported explanation of the colors of the rainbow, the colors often seen in cut glass! For thousands of years men had wondered about color, and had invented ingenious and intricate theories to explain its nature: White light was pure, while darkness impure . . . if one mixes pure and impure light in the proper proportion, a certain color will result . . . it all depends on how much darkness is added. Notions like these could be traced back to Aristotle!

There was no dearth of theories claiming to explain color in Newton's day. Descartes had a theory, Robert Hooke had a theory, Grimaldi had a theory. But no one, before Newton, had ever succeeded in devising experiments which established incontrovertible facts about light and color.

Although well received by English scientists, Newton's paper continued to be attacked on the Continent for about three years following its publication in the *Transactions*.

The Cambridge professor was mystified and somewhat amused by the objections of men like Huygens in Paris and Linus in Liége. He went to Barrow for an explanation of the strange attitude of well-known scientists to facts based on experiments which any one could repeat.

"They keep talking of their hypotheses as against mine," complained Newton. "As if an hypothesis was so important! But no one seems interested in performing the experiments himself—the most convincing argument of all!"

The older man smiled. His years of adversity, as well as his travels throughout the world, had given him a patient understanding of men. "Don't be disturbed, Mr. Newton. Men will defend an old, though erroneous, opinion as they would their dearest possession. It has been that way for a long time and one must expect it."

"But the facts, the facts established by my experiments are

what count," protested Newton. "My critics are annoyed because the evidence I present contradicts their notions of what color is. They expect the facts to fit the picture in their minds —instead of changing the picture to fit the facts!"

Dr. Barrow shook his head. "You are a pioneer in this field, Mr. Newton, and must expect rebuffs from those in high places. The idea of facts and experiments first, and hypotheses second, is new in our time. But it will have to be accepted by the world sooner or later, despite all opposition."

Before long, Newton's original enthusiasm over the publication of his paper vanished completely. At the urging of Oldenburg, the secretary of the Royal Society, he devoted considerable time to writing detailed answers to the objections offered by the Continental scientists.

"It was a great mistake," confessed the weary Newton to his roommate one evening, "for me ever to have published that paper on light. I can't think about my other work any more. All I seem to do is argue with my critics—most of whom refuse to listen to reason or to facts."

"But it may be all to the good," observed the optimistic Wickins. "Your name is now known all over Europe. You've succeeded in making a reputation for yourself in spite of this opposition."

"I don't need a reputation," murmured Newton. "It wastes too much of one's life. Often I think I'd be better off if no one were aware of my existence. At least my time and my thoughts would then be my own."

Gradually his critics came around, and soon Newton's work was universally accepted more and more for what it was: a well-planned series of experiments which established certain important facts about light and color. Lucas succeeded Linus at Liége, and proved more receptive to new ideas. The former claimed, however, that on repeating one of Newton's experiments he had obtained a shorter spectrum than the one described in the *Transactions*. At that time neither Lucas nor Newton realized that the discrepancy was due entirely to the different types of glass used in the prisms!

Newton was beginning to congratulate himself over the return of peace and quiet to his life when fresh trouble arose. An article written by Hooke was called to the Trinity professor's attention. It contained a violent attack on some of Newton's light theories; at the same time the writer went so far as to imply that a number of Newton's ideas on the subject had come from him, Hooke!

Again Isaac Newton began to wonder if it was all worth while? It seemed to him that anyone who found out something new was immediately assailed by his fellow men.

"Why all this bitterness?" he said to Oldenburg. "Hooke thinks light consists of waves; I think it is made up of particles. Both of these views are merely guesses or hypotheses. Perhaps both are true, for each explains certain facts not explained by the other. A hypothesis is not a mathematical law! It is only a picture in one's mind to help make facts more understandable."

By this time, Newton had learned more about Hooke from Barrow, who thought it best to prepare the young scientist for the world outside the University. Robert Hooke is known to the physics students of today for his law which states that, within elastic limits, stress is proportional to strain. And in the field of biology, Hooke has gone down to fame as the keen-eyed microscopist who gave the name "cell" to the tiny compartments he observed in thinly sliced sections of cork.

Hooke was as brilliant as he was vain and irritable. Burdened with a sickly body, his restless and ever-curious mind kept pushing into every area of the expanding science of his day. Interested in everything, his brain proved remarkably rich in creative ideas; indeed, Hooke had so many theories that he simply couldn't find the time to develop all of them. The result was that he frequently suspected his fellow scientists of appropriating his ideas as their own.

The scientific criticism in Hooke's article did not upset Newton. What did serve to infuriate the latter was the veiled accusation that he had plagiarized, or even stolen, another man's ideas. The angry Newton, feeling that his integrity had been attacked, decided to write an answer immediately. This turned out to be a hard-hitting masterpiece in which Hooke's claims and arguments were demolished one by one.

Not long after this painful incident, Newton lost all interest in the light controversy. He flatly refused to waste any more time and energy answering criticisms of his light theories. His own mind refused to produce new ideas as long as it was occupied with repeating or discussing old ones. And for the reserved, meditative Cambridge scholar there was a far greater thrill in pushing ahead into uncharted intellectual fields than in marking time in the known.

For the next few years, Isaac Newton tried to forget the world and sincerely hoped it would forget him. He expressed his attitude toward science in a letter to the gentle Oldenburg in these revealing words: "I will bid adieu to it eternally, excepting what I do for my private satisfaction, or leave to come after me; for I see a man must either resolve to put out nothing new, or to become a slave to defend it."

It was plain that the shy, reserved Trinity professor had been badly hurt by his first experience with the rough-and-tumble world!

11

THE DISPENSATION

Three years after he had relinquished the Lucasian Chair of Mathematics to Isaac Newton, Dr. Barrow was appointed Master of Trinity. Friends of the College congratulated themselves that, at last, it would be supervised by a man of courage, scholarship, and integrity.

The new Master had a difficult job on his hands. Fellowships at Trinity ran for seven years, during which time young scholars were expected to devote their time to studies leading to a divinity degree. In actual practice, there was no time limit; many with little taste for learning stayed on as Fellows for ten or twenty years because they enjoyed the secure income and the cultured college atmosphere.

The new Master of Trinity quickly perceived that reform measures would have to be instituted slowly. There was much resistance to change on the part of the older Fellows who disliked the thought of having to give up comfortable berths at Trinity for rural parsonages where they would have to exist on a poverty level. Barrow, a compassionate and understanding man, hoped to achieve his ends by tact and persuasion rather than by threats and compulsion.

About two years after he had become Master, Isaac Barrow

received some disturbing information in regard to the position of Newton at Trinity. For several days his keen mind mulled over the problem; finally he decided that he had no right to keep the matter from Newton any longer.

The Master of Trinity, immersed in his friend's problem, walked slowly across the quadrangle to what is now known as Newton's staircase, east of the Great Court. By the time he had climbed the stairs to the first floor, where Newton occupied rooms on the right side, Barrow had more or less decided on how to broach the subject to Trinity's leading scholar.

Newton was different, he said to himself. Lives in his own world, an insulated world. Must try not to shock him. He must be protected at all costs!

Barrow knocked and waited. He knocked again. At last Newton opened the door slowly, as if reluctant to admit anyone from the outside world into his chambers.

"Oh!" he exclaimed, looking pleased the moment he recognized his old friend. "Do come in, Dr. Barrow."

The older man entered and looked around curiously. There on the table was the dinner—gruel, bread, ale—and still uneaten although it was late in the evening. Probably his breakfast, too, had been removed untouched earlier in the day. . . . A good thing Newton had a strong constitution! Barrow said to himself. Work and study, study and work. He wondered how many men could maintain Newton's pace without collapsing?

"Working on your chemistry?" remarked Barrow, noting the many stains and holes in the young man's surplice.

"Yes, sir. In fact I just got back from my laboratory in the garden. I'm engaged in rebuilding my little furnace. You see, it doesn't get hot enough to melt certain metals," explained Newton.

"Doing the brick work yourself?" asked the older man.

"Oh, yes—I have to. I can't seem to find anyone to do it for me—at least, do it well."

Barrow sank into a chair; for a few moments there was absolute quiet in the room. Barrow hated to start on his unpleasant task.

"Don't be unnecessarily alarmed, Mr. Newton, at what I am about to say," the Master of Trinity began. "It's nothing more than a legal technicality. I am sure everything will turn out right—if properly handled."

Barrow studied the remote expression on his friend's face and again regretted the necessity of having to upset Newton.

"There's an old rule," he said casually, "which has just been called to my attention by a highly placed person. Probably I stepped on the toes of this individual in my efforts to effect changes at the College. At any rate, the rule is as follows: A Fellow at Trinity must enter Holy Orders after serving his seven-year period. It seems that this applies even to those Fellows who have been appointed to professorships." He stopped to study the effect of his words on the younger man.

For a few seconds there was no reaction. Newton's thoughts had been far from the practical world, the world of rules, and of men skilled in getting around rules. It was taking some time for the full significance of Barrow's remarks to strike home. . . .

"You mean—you mean that if I refuse to enter Holy Orders I'll lose my Fellowship?" Newton stared at his friend unbelievingly.

"I didn't say that, I didn't say that," repeated Barrow gently. "I merely stated the rule under which the College is supposed to operate. It is for you to decide, Mr. Newton, about Holy Orders. If you agree to enter, the matter is closed.

If you refuse—well, we'll simply find some way of getting around an unnecessarily rigid rule."

Isaac Newton shook himself as if half hoping to find it all a bad dream. He could no longer be a Fellow of Trinity! The entire foundation of his life, his thinking, his studies—was crumbling!

He had never given much thought to his security; it was something he had always taken for granted. But now—if he lost his Fellowship, he would certainly be removed from the Lucasian Chair of Mathematics! . . . Newton was beginning to look dazed, shaken.

The sympathetic Barrow understood what was passing though his friend's mind; and he suffered as he read the latter's face.

"Tell me, Mr. Newton, what your decision is—and we'll proceed from there," he suggested quietly.

Newton's lips tightened as he stared straight ahead stubbornly. He would not be pushed! Life had never beaten caution into him. He would fly in the face of the wind—not with it!

"I will not enter Holy Orders," Newton said quietly. "I can serve my religion better by remaining outside the Church."

"No doubt you can!" exclaimed Barrow, almost approvingly. And why not? For it was Barrow himself who had started Newton off on theological studies.

The Bible, for Newton, was the true basis of his faith. No doctrine was incontrovertible unless it had explicit Scriptural support. He and Barrow had spent many exciting days poring over old manuscripts as they studied the fascinating history of early Christianity. The Master of Trinity College was therefore fully prepared for Newton's refusal to be prudent, cautious.

"Now that we know where you stand, Mr. Newton, the next step is to plan a course of action," observed Barrow in a matter-of-fact way.

Newton looked surprised. "Is there anything that can be done?"

"Certainly! All is not lost—not by any means. We will prepare a petition to the Crown asking that an exception be made in your case. If the King grants this dispensation, you'll stay on as Fellow and continue as Lucasian professor."

The unworldly mathematician shook his head as if completely bewildered. "Do you think the King will pay any attention to a personal request? I don't see why he should grant such a dispensation—just for me."

Barrow rose to his feet and laughed. "Why? Because you are Newton and there are precious few like you in England! Also, you have friends who are important enough to make their influence felt. And I know people at the Court, too!"

The younger man was only slightly cheered by these words; they conjured up a world of which he was thoroughly ignorant.

"In a few days, you and I will draw up the petition to the King," continued Barrow, "and then we'll send it to the proper authorities. When the time comes, you will be called to London for a hearing."

Before his friend departed, Newton thanked him in a low, dispirited voice. The interview had been almost as painful for the Master as for the Fellow. What the former had kept from the troubled Newton was the fact that only recently, in a similar case, Francis Aston, had had his petition turned down. And Aston had failed in spite of the strong support of Sir Joseph Williamson, Secretary of State!

But why tell poor Newton that? Barrow hoped that some thoughtless friend would not call the attention of the pessimistic professor to the Aston case. Actually, the Master of Trinity was confident that, properly presented and energetically supported by important scientists, Newton's petition would prove successful. After all, Charles II was interested in science, and therefore must have some inkling of the petitioner's invaluable contributions to science and mathematics.

He'll be all right, Barrow kept assuring himself. Rule or no rule, a Newton cannot be dropped so easily. But what if they did? Barrow shook his head. He didn't even want to think of that possibility. . . .

The next few weeks were full of worry and strain for Newton. With the advice and aid of Barrow, he composed the petition to the King. The older man, experienced in the ways of the Court, insisted that Newton himself journey to London early in February, 1675, and plan to remain there until the matter came to a decision. There would be important people to see, and he, Barrow, would furnish the necessary letters of introduction. It should not be too unpleasant an experience, he kept asuring Newton. Once over, it would soon be forgotten.

Not too unpleasant . . . not too unpleasant! In the meantime, Newton found it impossible to concentrate on his studies or experiments. His mind, a delicately adjusted mechanism, could only work smoothly when no personal problems disturbed it. It was only after everyday problems had been banished from his thoughts that Newton could force his mind to obey his will.

When hard at work, he would become almost completely detached from physical existence. His thoughts were constantly being stirred, arranged and rearranged—in the stillness of his mind as he waited patiently for the thrilling *moment of illumination.*

Asleep or awake, his mind brooded continually over some problem; often the long-sought solution would slip into view during the first few minutes of his awakening from a deep sleep. Hence Newton's lifelong habit of sitting motionless on the edge of his bed every morning, as he tried to recapture a fleeting thought which had occurred to him as sleep ended.

How different things were now! His mind was in a state of turmoil and simply refused to produce ideas. It was preoccupied with the future only. With the Fellowship lost—what would he do? Be a gentleman farmer at Woolesthorpe? Ah, for the years when he had nothing to think about but his work!

Newton resented the necessity of having to ask help from bureaucrats, politicians, hangers-on at the Court. The Trinity professor was filled with humiliation at the very thought. Although he had been brought up as a Royalist sympathizer, Newton was by this time a confirmed Whig. This meant that he was suspicious of royal prerogatives and "the good old ways." He was now a warm supporter of the rising democracy which had been strengthened by the Puritan government of Cromwell. The fact that, in his present difficulty, he would have to seek the aid of dyed-in-the-wool Royalists made it all the more painful!

Frantically his agitated mind cast about for steps to take in the meantime. He decided that the first thing to do was to resign from the Royal Society—immediately! His dues were already in arrears, and a childish fear made him feel that in the dismal future the required shilling a week would prove an intolerable burden on his finances.

Yes, he must write to Oldenburg at once and explain that he was resigning because the distance from Cambridge to London made it inconvenient to attend the weekly meetings of the Royal Society!

When Oldenburg received the letter of resignation, he was furious. Not understanding Newton's feverish state of mind, the secretary of the Society attributed it all to Newton's annoyance over Hooke's bitter criticism.

"That Newton is oversensitive!" he exclaimed to a friend. "Hooke's attacks are vicious and uncalled for—but that's no reason for Newton to resign. I won't let him do it! The entire membership will be up in arms if he drops out of the Society. Hooke or no Hooke, Newton must stay with us!"

Oldenburg got busy and before long Newton received a note informing him that, by order of the council of the Royal Society, he would be excused from paying dues—in return for a promise to communicate his experiments and ideas to the Society. Newton, much calmer by this time, dropped the matter and retained his membership.

Early in February, 1675, he caught the coach for London in accordance with Barrow's suggestion. It was a dismal trip, for his mind kept magnifying the unpleasantness ahead. Newton stayed on for about six weeks, spending a good deal of the time waiting in the anterooms of the influential people who, according to the Master of Trinity, simply had to be enlisted on the petitioner's side.

The sights of London meant little to the scholar from Cambridge, absorbed as he was in his own problems. He was a mere onlooker at the fashionable world where men affected long curled hair which reached down to their shoulders. The dandies of that time also had a strange fondness for little muffs which dangled elegantly from ribbons around their necks. Nor was Newton interested in the false curls on wires worn by the ladies, and the extremely wide skirts from which the wire hoops had only recently been removed.

The streets were filthy . . . gangs of ruffians roamed about at night and made it dangerous for honest citizens to venture forth. There were coffeehouses everywhere; they were like clubs where men of similar interests or profession met to talk or transact business. The patrons of the coffeehouses sat at the tables with their hats on, and spitting on the floor was a more or less common practice at the time.

The Cambridge professor was cheered by the respect and attention he received in London, and soon became less melancholy about the future. To Newton's surprise his name was known wherever he appeared; and he was continually assured that the King would certainly grant his petition.

Soon Newton decided that this particular experience was exactly what he had needed. Everyone should have to humble himself on occasion for the good of his soul, he said to himself. Some find it necessary to go through the ordeal often during a lifetime. Why should he complain at having to do it once?

Taking advantage of his enforced stay in the metropolis, he dropped in at the regular Wednesday meeting of the Royal Society, whose quarters at the time consisted of a few rooms in Gresham College. Oldenburg was overjoyed at seeing Newton, and promptly introduced the distinguished visitor to everyone present.

Although he had never attended a meeting before, Newton found that the members seemed to know all about him. By this time the news of his petition had leaked out, and a number of people at the meeting assured him that the King would definitely grant a dispensation in his case. All in all, it was a heartwarming afternoon for Isaac Newton.

"You have the fullest public support," cried Oldenburg. "No one in his right mind would want to see you separated from Trinity. It would be a national calamity!"

Newton relaxed. He went to two other meetings, at one of which Hooke was expected to repeat Newton's prism experiment—certain details of which had been criticized abroad. But Hooke didn't perform it, much to the visitor's disappointment. Instead, the former read an excellent paper on the diffraction and interference of light.

On March 12, 1675, His Majesty, Charles II, signed the all-important indulgence and dispensation. It stated that Isaac Newton could retain his Trinity Fellowship without entering Holy Orders for *as long as* he held the Luscasian Professorship!

A relieved and elated Newton hurried back to Cambridge with his precious dispensation; he knew Barrow would be overjoyed. And Newton himself wanted nothing more than to get back to work. He felt he had wasted entirely too much time on personal problems. . . .

Several weeks later Oldenburg received an apologetic note from Newton. It seemed that the latter had met an "Ancient Gentleman" at one of the meetings of the Society. This gentleman was hard of hearing and had asked Newton for detailed information about a certain improved type of ear trumpet. The Cambridge professor had promised to send a complete description of the instrument to the old gentleman. Owing to the pressure of other business, the matter had slipped from Newton's mind.

Enclosed was the description requested. Would Oldenburg be so kind as to transmit it, along with apologies for the delay, to the "Ancient Gentleman"?

12

HOOKE AGAIN!

One bitter cold morning in the winter of 1676, John Collins made his way to the Royal Society office in the Royal Exchange building in London.

Oldenburg guessed the reason for the visit the moment he saw the genial and devoted friend of science. It must be about Newton, he said to himself. The silence of the Cambridge professor was a problem not only to Oldenburg, Collins and the Royal Society, but also to English science.

"I've come to discuss what we can do about Newton," said Collins after they had exchanged greetings.

"You've read the explanation he sent me, Mr. Collins. He says that science wearies him and that he will have nothing more to do with it."

The visitor shook his head sadly. "I know—I've just returned from Cambridge."

Oldenburg sat up in his chair. "What did he say to you?"

"What did he say? Nothing! He has other interests now. And, as he says, he is doing the work that gives him the most pleasure."

"And what is that, may I ask?" Oldenburg looked puzzled.

"Chemistry which borders on alchemy," answered Collins

with a sigh. "Newton has been communicating with Boyle and is now fascinated by mercury, amalgams, mysterious chemical processes, and what not. What a waste of a great intellect!"

"And nothing else?" persisted Oldenburg.

Collins snorted. "Oh, yes—new types of ear trumpets . . . and theology and geography and cider-making and the repair of buildings at Woolesthorpe."

Oldenburg remained silent for a few seconds. He recalled the events of a few years back. Newton had published his final and devastating answer to Hooke's claims concerning light.

After that—silence from Newton! Why should a man put out a new idea if he had to become "a slave to defend it"? the Cambridge scientist had asked.

Light, according to Newton, consisted of very small particles emitted by luminous bodies through space at an enormous velocity. The rival hypothesis, put forth by Huygens, maintained that light, like sound, was a form of wave motion.

Newton's own attitude toward the conflicting theories was not as dogmatic as that of his followers. He could see that both explained certain phenomena equally well. However, he rejected the wave theory because of two considerations: first, it required the presence of a mysterious medium called the ether, which filled all space, but whose existence it was impossible to prove. Second, the wave theory failed to account for the indisputable fact that light, unlike sound, travels in straight lines.

During the century which followed his work, Newton's corpuscular theory became dominant both at home and abroad. However, after 1800, as the result of the experiments of Young and Fresnel, the wave theory began to be regarded as the more acceptable. Interference experiments proved that light must be a form of wave motion; polarization experiments proved that light waves are *tranverse*, i.e., the vibrations are at right angles to the direction of propagation. Interestingly enough, the physics of the twentieth century has found it necessary to return to a modified form of Newton's discarded corpuscular theory!

By this time Oldenburg had shaken himself out of his reverie. "How does Newton look to you, Mr. Collins—contented or restless? What the secretary hoped to hear was that the Trinity Fellow's retreat to private life was only temporary.

"That's just the point!" cried Collins. "He is completely absorbed by what he is doing. He's seldom out of his surplice . . . spends days and nights fussing in his laboratory. He doesn't bother to eat regularly—and when he does it is while standing and thinking of other things. His hair is changing from gray to white—and Newton is only about thirty-five years old. And he has less regard than ever for his personal appearance; he won't even stop to comb his hair! That's Newton for you! Pure mind, pure intellectual insight. But what is he doing with it now?"

"Did you try reasoning with him?" Oldenburg asked his anguished caller.

"I did, but it was hopeless. He has lost interest in mathematics and physics—the very subjects in which he excels. Instead, he wastes his precious time on trifling matters!"

"He doesn't care, he doesn't care," Oldenburg kept repeating. "Leibnitz will end up getting all the credit for Newton's discovery," he predicted gloomily.

To some of his friends Newton had shown the method of fluxions from which developed the differential calculus—the indispensable tool of modern science. Leibnitz was acquainted with Newton's paper "On Analysis" with its suggestion of the fluxion method; and the English mathematicians were well aware that the keen mind of Leibnitz was now turning to problems similar to those Newton had concentrated on earlier.

"Mark my words, Mr. Collins," exclaimed the agitated secretary, "Leibnitz will walk away with the prize while Newton dreams! All I could get from Newton, after much prodding, were two communications on the subject. And what did he do but keep his explanations confined to the infinite series! About fluxions, he only hints. And a hint is not enough to establish priority."

"There doesn't seem anything we can do about it," remarked Collins sadly as he was about to depart. "Newton isn't like other men. You can't tempt him with fame, glory, prizes. . . . He is sufficient unto himself—more so than any man I have ever known."

Collins paused in the doorway for a few moments and then added, "I sometimes think he is like a musician. Newton gets pleasure out of using his brain. It doesn't matter what he uses it for; it doesn't matter what tune it plays. As long as he can produce ideas, Newton is content. What a wonderful talent! It makes the entire external world shrink to insignificance."

Oldenburg understood what Collins meant. It wasn't mere pride or reserve or shyness on the part of Newton. It was simply that he lived an exciting life within himself. What the world might value highly, Newton would shrug off as foolish, vain; and what Newton might value highly, the world would smile at as childish.

"We'll have to be patient and perhaps he'll come around," was Oldenburg's final comment. "Newton can't be pushed into things he doesn't want to do. He's a stubborn man, Newton is, and there's no use trying to argue with him."

For the next two years, the situation remained unchanged. No one knew with what the Cambridge professor's mind was occupied; he continued to lecture on whatever subjects interested him. Most of his leisure time was spent on chemistry or alchemy—the line between the two being far from distinct at that time. In addition, he was drawn into an exhaustive study of the Bible, probably as the result of Barrow's earlier influence.

Isaac Barrow had died in the meantime, after five years as Master of Trinity. His death was a severe blow to Newton; now that his good friend and counselor was gone, he felt more alone than ever. Perhaps because of this feeling, theology became even dearer to Newton, for the late Dr. Barrow had loved this difficult subject and had inspired his protégé with a desire to learn more and more about its complexities.

When Oldenburg died, about a year after Barrow, Newton lost still another good friend. Robert Hooke and Dr. Nehemiah Grew were elected joint secretaries of the Royal Society to replace the earnest refugee scholar.

In November of 1679, Newton received a letter from the new secretary. In it, Hooke politely asked the Cambridge professor for communications on scientific matters. The Royal Society, the letter writer suggested, was anxious to hear from its distinguished member. Such communications would of course be private—unless Newton agreed to their publication. Hooke went on to point out that he, personally, had no feeling of antagonism toward his Cambridge colleague. Trouble or misunderstandings between them in the past was the work of childish individuals who delighted in stirring up an enmity for which there was no real basis. . . .

The rest of Hooke's letter was devoted to news from the world of science . . . Mallemont de Messanges and his new theory concerning the circular orbits of planets . . . the astronomer Flamsteed's latest observations . . . and so forth.

Newton had received a note of a similar nature from Hooke

three years before; at that time, the former had sent a gracious reply—but no scientific ideas. On the receipt of this second letter, however, Newton decided to answer Hooke in a way which would prove to the secretary that he, Newton, was nursing no bitterness.

I'll write Hooke a friendly letter, said Newton to himself, I'll tell him how honored I feel that he should ask me for opinions on "the celestial motion of planets" and the "laws and causes of springiness." It will give me an opportunity to explain that I am disinterested in science and mathematics. Perhaps the Royal Society will then stop insisting that I send them my ideas on those subjects. . . .

At the last moment Newton decided to add to this letter to Hooke an item which would "sweeten his answer"—as he later described it. Hooke loved experiments. Good! He would give the new secretary one to work on. Hooke would be satisfied and the Society pleased. Why not?

The idea had to do with the earth's rotation on its axis once every twenty-four hours. Instead of proving the rotation from the changing position of the sun and stars, Newton had thought of a way of proving it directly—something no one had ever succeeded in doing. It had occurred to him while he was busy with other matters.

As the earth moves, everything—buildings, trees, people—moves with it. Actually every object on the surface of the earth is constantly describing a giant circle around the axis. But we jump up and seem to land on the same spot we jumped from; we throw a ball into the air and it drops back into our hands because of gravity, in a vertical line—which means a line passing through the center of the earth. There is no direct evidence that we are moving in a circular path around the earth's axis at about a thousand miles an hour for the simple reason that everything moves—and therefore nothing seems to move!

Newton reasoned in this fashion: The higher an object is above the earth, the farther it is from the center of the earth—and the larger the circle it must describe around the earth's axis. And if an object is high enough above the surface of the earth, the larger circle it passes over must reveal itself in some way. Take a wheel spinning rapidly on an axle. A point on the rim of the wheel moves faster than a point near the hub. Why? Because, in an equal time, the former must move over a larger circle than the latter.

All this was simple, all this was understood. Now, said Newton, let us apply the same principle to a stone dropped from a height to the ground directly, or vertically, below it. The stone would not strike the spot directly below it! It would strike the ground somewhat *east* of the perpendicular owing to the rotation of the earth!

Newton explained why, in his letter to Hooke. The stone, before it is dropped, has a greater circular velocity than the point on the ground directly below it. This was so because the stone was moving faster in its larger circle than was the point on the ground in its smaller circle. And since the earth moves from west to east, the faster-moving stone would strike slightly *east* of the point on the ground below it!

Newton sent off the letter outlining the above experiment and promptly forgot all about it. On receiving the communication, Hooke read it to the assembled members of the Society. The proposed experiment aroused great interest; it was easy to grasp, and there was a general eagerness to test Newton's prediction. Hooke was congratulated on his success in breaking through the stubborn silence of the illustrious member from Trinity.

During the next week, while preparations were being made

for the experiment, Hooke had time to mull over Newton's suggestions. The secretary decided that the latter had made a mistake. An object dropped from a height would fall *south* of *east* rather than *east*, as Newton had stated. Also, Hooke was of the opinion that the path followed by the falling body would not be the spiral Newton said it would be—but more nearly an ellipse, or an "excentrical" ellipsoid.

Here at last was a chance to "polish off" Newton! Hooke could not resist taking advantage of this rare opportunity—even though he had assured Newton, in their correspondence, that future disagreements between them would be carried on in strict privacy. So at the very next meeting of the Society, the secretary lectured the members on what he considered errors in Newton's thinking.

When news of this reached Cambridge, Newton was annoyed both with Hooke and himself. If he had suspected that so much was going to be made of a little suggestion, he would have thought it out more thoroughly. Newton wrote to Hooke at once and said he agreed that a body in the latitude of London would fall to the southeast. However, he did not see eye to eye with Hooke concerning the nature of the path the falling body would take.

When the experiment was finally performed by the Royal Society, it was found that the body did fall to the southeast. Newton received the news of the successful outcome of his idea with little enthusiasm. He remained somewhat disturbed over his own carelessness as well as over Hooke's failure to keep their compact to thrash out differences in private.

Robert Hooke had scored for once! As it turned out, the secretary's minor triumph was indirectly responsible for pushing Newton on to the greatest accomplishment of his career!

The problem of the exact path of a falling body struck Newton as being a complicated mathematical puzzle—and he was a genius at such puzzles. Immediately his thinking turned once again to mathematical lines. Hooke's remarks had aroused his curiosity and he suddenly remembered his interest in the same problem back in the plague years at Woolesthorpe. . . .

Everything else stopped for Newton during the next few weeks. There was no rest for his inquiring mind. He simply had to solve this old problem. What he sought was a mathematical solution, clear and decisive.

What must be the path of a planet around a central body like our sun? Would it be possible to calculate the exact curve, assuming that the attractive force influencing the planet varied inversely as the square of the distance? The inverse square law again! Twice as far away, one fourth of the attractive force; three times as far, one ninth of the attractive force. . . .

Finally he got it! Newton's mind danced as he went over his mathematical proof. It was correct. The path would be an ellipse! Yes, an ellipse! Now that he had it all down on paper, it seemed simple, very simple.

He had accomplished what he had set out to do. Now he must go back to his chemistry. He pushed the slip of paper on which he had made his calculations into a drawer full of other notes—and promptly forgot the matter.

The puzzle had been solved, his curiosity satisfied. The orbit of a planet no longer interested him.

13

WREN'S OFFER

Three men sat around a small table in a coffeehouse near the Royal Exchange building in London. It was a bright January afternoon in 1684, and they had just come from a meeting of the Royal Society.

Sir Christopher Wren, the oldest of the group, was already the most famous architect of his time; the magnificent churches, which he built to replace those destroyed by the Fire of London which occurred in 1666, bear witness to his genius. Robert Hooke, the eminent scientist, pale, tense, his body racked with pain, was the second man. And the third was the young, impulsive astronomer and physicist Edmund Halley,

There was much table talk concerning planets, the paths they follow and why their orbits cannot be circular. Hooke, as usual, expressed his opinions with an air of mystery. He could tell more—but this was not the time for it. Before long, he would reveal something which would clear up many puzzling facts—and startle the world.

Wren, who was an astronomer as well as an architect, seemed annoyed by Hooke's manner. Why doesn't the man stop hinting and say what he thinks? he said to himself. Wren and Halley exchanged glances which seemed to say, "Good old Hooke! He never changes!"

Finally Wren decided that he had had enough. "Gentlemen," he said, as he leaned forward and eyed his companions thoughtfully, "let me state the problem which is baffling us. Perhaps a simple statement will clear the air. Shall I try?"

"An excellent idea, Sir Christopher!" cried Halley. "It always helps to know exactly what one doesn't know."

"Yes, let's have it," agreed Hooke.

Wren stroked his chin for a few moments as he concentrated on the wording of his statement. "I'll try—and I hope you gentlemen will correct me if I should stray."

"The orbits of the plants are elliptical," he began. "I think we are in agreement on that?"

His companions nodded.

"Next—we all suspect that there is a force which attracts a planet to the sun, and this force—which we call gravity—diminishes as the square of the distance. Any dissent so far, gentlemen?"

No objections were offered.

Wren's manner became more precise. "Finally—and this is the crux of the matter—all three of us feel that there is a definite mathematical relationship between the two statements I just made. In other words, the orbit of a planet is an ellipse because the force of gravity falls off as the square of the distance."

"Well put, Sir Christopher!" exclaimed the excitable Halley. "That's the story in an nutshell."

"Yes, indeed, very well expressed," murmured Hooke.

"And thus the matter stands," continued Wren. "We have strong suspicions and weak proofs. The relationship between elliptical orbit and inverse square law must be shown mathematically. Words won't help. The proof must be clean, stark

—that is, mathematical. And that is where we have all bogged down, gentlemen."

"I, for one, must confess that the mathematics of the problem has been beyond my modest powers so far," noted Halley with a shrug.

"And if you find it too much, Mr. Halley, then my efforts will certainly be fruitless," observed Wren graciously.

Hooke felt their eyes upon him. "I feel confident, gentlemen, that the inverse square law can explain the motion through the sky of every heavenly body—yes, every heavenly body."

"That may well be. But can you prove it, sir?" asked Wren.

Hooke smiled and looked away, as if undecided about what to reveal to his colleagues. "I have the proof, gentlemen, I have it. But for the present I prefer not to make it public. Perhaps people will learn to value it more—when I do publish it."

Halley and Wren exchanged quick glances. There was Hooke up to his old tricks again! He knew but he wouldn't tell. What childishness!

Suddenly Wren had a thought. This time Hooke wasn't going to escape so lightly, he said to himself.

"Let me offer a prize, gentlemen," said Wren, "in the form of a book of the value of forty shillings. Whoever brings me a convincing solution of the problem within two months will receive the prize!"

Halley laughed. "A generous offer, I must say. I'll compete —but I'm rather dubious about winning."

"Don't give up, Mr. Halley. Remember—forty shillings is forty shillings! And how about you, Mr. Hooke?" asked Wren.

The secretary of the Royal Society rose and began to struggle into his heavy coat. "I have the proof, Sir Christopher," he answered with a confident smile, "and will produce it at the proper time."

And so ended the coffeehouse meeting which was destined to play such an important role in the history of science!

Just before the group broke up outside the coffeehouse, Wren managed to whisper to Halley: "I don't think Hooke has the proof . . . merely one of his claims. I'm sure he won't turn up with it."

Sir Christopher Wren was right. Hooke did not deliver his proof and the forty-shilling prize went unclaimed. Two months passed . . . three . . . four. Still no word from Robert Hooke!

Halley became impatient. The matter was too important to be put off. Some scientist on the Continent might stumble on the solution while Hooke dallied. It was apparent that the mathematics involved was too much for the latter—or he would have been heard from long ago.

"I'm going to Cambridge to see Newton," Halley announced to Wren when August of 1684 rolled around.

"Newton? Why Newton?"

"Because he has an experimental mind and is a natural mathematician. What combination could be rarer?" explained Halley. "At any rate, we have nothing to lose. I have a feeling that he may help us."

Halley had learned about Newton's mathematical talent from John Collins. The former remembered with what ease the young Trinity Fellow had once solved the complicated annuity problems presented by Collins.

Acting on his "hunch," Halley hurried to Cambridge late in August. He found Newton puttering in his garden chemical laboratory. Since they had once been introduced at a Royal Society meeting some years before, the two men spent the first few minutes chatting about the affairs of that organization.

Soon the visitor decided it was time to get down to the business he had in mind. "I've come here, Mr. Newton, to ask you to help us with a mathematical problem which we, at the Royal Society, can't seem to solve."

Halley paused and examined the older man's impassive face for a moment. "What, sir," he continued, "would be the exact curve or orbit of a planet around the sun—if we supposed that gravity diminished as the square of the distance?"

It was precisely the problem which had occupied Newton during the plague years at Woolesthorpe—eighteen years ago! And it was precisely the problem to which he had returned only five years before—after Hooke had loudly caught him in error on the occasion of the falling body experiment described in the previous chapter.

Newton eyed Halley for a moment and then without a trace of hesitation answered, "An ellipse, sir."

Halley almost jumped with surprise. So Newton knew!

"How do you know it would be an ellipse, Mr. Newton?" he asked in amazement.

"Because I have calculated it," answered the older man simply.

By this time the excitable Edmund Halley was breathing hard. "Do you have the calculations, Mr. Newton?"

The absent-minded professor began to search through an assortment of papers in the drawers of his writing table. It wasn't there. He went through them again. There were many scraps of paper but the one Halley was so anxious to lay his hands on—could not be found!

Newton began to feel that it would be a waste of time to search any longer. "I'll have to calculate it over again for you,

Mr. Halley. I'm sorry it's lost—but it's been several years since I worked it out."

Halley tried to hide his disappointment. "Will you be so kind as to send it to me as soon as you have repeated your calculations, Mr. Newton?"

"I'll send it to you," promised Newton, somewhat puzzled by his visitor's unusual interest.

In November of that year, the promised calculation was delivered by a Mr. Paget, a young mathematician who acted as courier.

Halley was delighted, and as his eyes swept over the mathematical proof he became almost ecstatic. "I'm glad Newton didn't forget, I'm glad Newton didn't forget," he repeated.

Paget smiled. "No danger of that, sir. As a matter of fact, your visit seems to have started him off on a new line—or perhaps sent him back to an old line. Newton has been busy since October preparing lectures on this and related subjects."

"I'm glad to hear it, Mr. Paget. What can be more important than determining the exact path of heavenly bodies," remarked Halley joyfully.

To the young astronomer, the proof he had just received from Newton was pure gold! Halley regarded it as too valuable to be concealed from the world any longer. This contribution should be shouted from the housetops! he said to himself.

It wasn't long before the tireless Halley again journeyed to Cambridge. He simply couldn't rest until he had convinced Newton that the precious mathematical proof should be published. As a member of the Royal Society, he was aware of the Cambridge professor's aversion to publicity. He'll come around if approached properly, Halley kept assuring himself. Perhaps the old wounds were healed by this time. . . .

When he got to Newton's quarters, Halley sat down and talked of London and politics and the Royal Society and the

Court. The Cambridge scholar listened politely and tried to display an interest in the world outside of Cambridge, a world about which he knew so little.

"I understand," observed Halley, merely to make conversation, "that you have been lecturing on planetary motion since my visit here in August."

Newton nodded. "I suppose you did start me off again on matters that had once interested me. Yes, I've been working on several lectures. Here are my lecture notes. In a way, you are responsible for them, Mr. Halley."

The visitor picked up the manuscript out of curiosity and began to study it. The title was *De Motu Corporum*, or *Concerning the Motion of Bodies*. As Halley read on, his body became tense. Here was the proof Newton had sent him on the elliptical orbits of planets. But that wasn't all! Newton had expanded the "ellipse" idea. . . . He had generalized. . . . He was now concerned not only with the sun and the planets but also with the motion of *all* particles in free space. . . .

Halley did not have time to grasp it all, but he understood enough to perceive that everything in the lecture notes was original, mathematical and beautifully developed. Now, he wasn't merely interested in obtaining Newton's permission to publish the proof which Paget had brought him a month before; he wanted the *De Motu* and wanted it intensely.

Halley felt it was of immense importance to have this unusual manuscript entered upon the register of the Royal Society. This would immediately establish Newton's priority in regard to the ideas in *De Motu*. After that he must get Newton to agree to its publication. *De Motu* was of tremendous significance . . . an epoch-making contribution to physics and astronomy. But the matter of publication had to be approached gradually, the tactful Halley decided. The self-effacing professor must be handled just right.

"You must send this to the Royal Society as soon as possible," cried Halley, waving the manuscript in the air. "The world has been awaiting it for a long time. Like a thunderstorm, your ideas will clear the air of the many vague and false notions that have possessed the minds of men for ages!"

Newton was taken aback—and pleased—at the young astronomer's honest enthusiasm. The world awaiting . . . the world awaiting. . . . The oversensitive Cambridge scholar wondered if this meant the beginning of still another controversy?

He could not, however, resist the younger man's sincere interest and breathless excitment. Yes, he would send his *De Motu* to the Society as soon as it had been completed and corrected.

When Halley got back to London, he just couldn't sit still. He buttonholed members of the Royal Society and poured the wonderful news about Newton into their ears. His enthusiasm proved so contagious that the Society officially delegated Halley and Paget to keep after Newton and see that he did not forget his promise.

The manuscript reached the Royal Society in February, 1685. But by this time Newton, largely because of Halley's tact and encouragement, had thrown himself into an all-out attack on the entire problem of gravitation. Thus the *De Motu* itself became only a starting point, a small part of the tremendous whole which was rapidly opening before his mind. Already it was showing signs of developing into Newton's masterwork, the greatest intellectual achievement in the history of science!

For the next seventeen months, Newton was barely alive in the sense that most of us understand the word. Food, drink, sleep, body, feeling—none of these mattered to him. He lived only in his mind where theorems, propositions, proofs, problems—and only these—held complete sway over his being. It was an exhausting ordeal; but once he had begun, Newton with characteristic obstinacy would not turn back. A hard taskmaster, he insisted on driving his mind without letup regardless of what the inhuman pace might do to his health.

"He doesn't eat. How can a man live without eating?" complained Deborah, an elderly woman whose job it was to make Newton's bed and tidy up his room.

A youth named Humphrey Newton happened to be Isaac Newton's assistant or amanuensis at that time. Though the former, too, came from the vicinity of Grantham, he was not related to his employer.

"Oh, he eats—sometimes," remarked Humphrey. "If I keep reminding him that his food is waiting, Mr. Newton will sometimes stop for a bite or two—while standing up."

"Why doesn't he sit down and eat like other men?" continued Deborah, looking concerned.

Humphrey laughed. "Because he is Isaac Newton and for him thought comes before food. There sits his dinner cold and untouched—as usual. So what can you do, Deborah, but take it away and bring on his supper?"

"And what will happen to the supper?"

"Who knows? Perhaps tomorrow morning you'll remove that—untouched—when you bring him his breakfast."

The gray-haired bedmaker shook her head. It was true that she profited indirectly from Mr. Newton's strange eating habits, for she would eat what he didn't—rather than see it go to waste. But Mr. Newton was such a kind gentleman, she said to herself. If he kept forgeting to eat for much longer, something dreadful was bound to happen to him! She had been a bedmaker at Cambridge for many years and had seen scholars go to pieces more than once. . . .

Humphrey read her thoughts and smiled. "Don't worry about Mr. Newton, Deborah. He has a strong body. Who else could work day and night the way he does without breaking down? Why, I don't believe he sleeps more than three or four hours a night—ever. He says he can't spare the time!"

"But why can't what he's doing be put aside while he dines?" cried the distressed Deborah. "What harm if he finishes his work a week or two later?"

"That I can't answer," said Humphrey with a shrug. "Only Mr. Newton understands why he grudges the time spent sleeping or eating. Do you know what he does when really exhausted?"

Deborah shook her head.

"He retires to his laboratory and spends an afternoon on his chemical experiments—for recreation!"

The woman's face became apprehensive. "I don't think it's good, I don't think it's good. Mr. Newton never used to be this way except for a short time. But this has been going on for months."

Humphrey moved to the window overlooking the garden where Newton could be seen slowly pacing back-and-forth, lost in thought. The absorbed professor's hair was uncombed; his shoes were down at the heels; his surplice soiled and creased.

"Just watch him, Deborah," said Humphrey as if he were talking of someone completely incomprehensible. "Soon he'll capture the idea he's been seeking. Then he'll run up the stairs madly and rush to the table here to write the precious thought down before he forgets it. That's Isaac Newton for you!"

Deborah peered out of the window to see. The two waited for a few minutes. Soon their patience was rewarded. Isaac Newton's mind had struck something important. His body was galvanized into action. He was making for the stairs leading to his chambers. And his expression was one of joy—almost rapture!

"I can't understand such scholars, I can't understand them," murmured Deborah as she hurried out the door—bearing Newton's untouched dinner.

Food didn't matter nor did sleep, for Isaac Newton was wholly absorbed with first principles which he was expressing in beautifully clear, mathematical language. His mind was in the process of giving birth to his great *Principia*, whose full Latin title is *Philosophiae Naturalis Principia Mathematica* (Mathematical Principles of Natural Philosophy).

It is this magnificent work which has often been described as the most extraordinary production of the human mind.

14

THE PRINCIPIA

"In nature," said Newton in his *Principia,* "like effects are produced by like causes, as breathing in a man and in a beast, as the fall of stones in Europe and in America, the light of a kitchen fire and the sun, the reflection of light on the earth and the planets."

The emphasis throughout this imposing book was on *how* things happen—not *why* they happen. Newton was convinced that the laws of the universe could be discovered only by the experimental approach.

One should begin with experimentally established facts and then build up to a theory, argued Newton. The other way, the "armchair" approach with its endless debating of what is or isn't true, can only lead to uncertain conclusion. The Newtonian outlook was new and revolutionary; his insistence that experiments must come first was unacceptable to many of the leading scientists of his time.

Halley watched the development of Newton's *Principia* during the months following his November, 1684, visit with the personal interest of a father in the accomplishments of a beloved child.

"He's finally got it, he's finally got it!" he exclaimed to

Wren one day after a hasty trip to Cambridge. "The way is clear now. Newton has managed to solve his key problem."

"And what was that?" asked Wren, struck by his friend's excitement.

"The problem of points," explained Halley, "the very problem which, as long as it remained unsolved, kept Newton from announcing his law of gravitation almost twenty years ago. Even our calm Lucasian professor looked flushed and shaken when he told me of his success—and what could be more unusual?"

"I don't recall the problem," said Wren.

"It's a fundamental one. At Woolesthorpe, during the plague years, he was stopped by the thought that his law of gravitation was only approximate. His calculations were based on the supposition that the sun and the planets, or the earth and the moon, exerted their attractions as if they were mere points in space. How could he be sure the actual size of the sun or earth ought not to be considered in his calculations? An apple three inches in diameter and an earth eight thousand miles in diameter attract each other. How could he dare disregard the vast difference in size between the two?"

"And you say he's gotten around that difficulty?" said Wren with rising interest.

"Exactly! That's why I felt like shouting the news through the streets of London when I heard that Newton had finally accomplished the impossible. He has proven mathematically that as far as gravitation is concerned the sun and planets may be treated as points in space. And a beautiful mathematical proof it turned out to be!"

"How about practical verification?" said Wren thoughtfully.

Halley laughed. "He has it, Sir Christopher, he has it. Newton went over his old calculations of the force of gravity at the distance of the moon. He used Picard's latest figure for the earth's actual radius. And this time Newton's results were almost perfect: the moon falls toward the earth exactly as demanded by his law of gravitation! Yes, the apple and the moon obey the same law!"

Halley could well be proud of the momentous work he had helped bring into the world. The *Principia* became an inexhaustible treasure chest for scientists during the next two hundred years. To write it Newton had to sift all the available knowledge of his time and gather what was valid, important. He then proceeded to arrange and organize the mountain of facts and concepts until grand patterns began to emerge. For the first time in the history of human thought, a mathematical understanding of the physical world became possible.

He made use of the labors of Galileo and went on to formulate what the world has since called Newton's laws of motion. Newton generalized the law of attraction: not only the apple and the moon, but every particle of matter in the universe attracts every other particle with a force which varies directly as the product of their masses and inversely as the square of the distance between them. Concepts like mass and weight and acceleration and momentum, he defined clearly for the first time.

Newton went on to waves and tides and acoustics—or the science of sounds—and showed how the principles he had established could be applied in those fields. He developed a mathematical treatment of the solar system, his *System of the World*, making use of the theorems explained in the first book of his *Principia*. How to calculate the mass of the sun and the masses and distances of the planes . . . the causes of the perturbations of the moon . . . the theory of tides . . . how to determine the orbit of a comet from three observations. . . .

THE *PRINCIPIA*

In this tremendous work Newton laid the foundation and erected the framework of a structure whose completion, during the next two hundred years, was successfully achieved by the world's greatest mathematicians and physicists. The *Principia* was written in Latin, at that time the international language of science; the lack of illustration plus its concise style made it extremely difficult reading.

The forty-two-year-old Cambridge professor definitely did not have the general reader in mind when he wrote the *Principia;* it was aimed rather at the few who possessed the necessary mathematical and scientific background. In fact, Newton advised those with average mathematical understanding not to waste time trying to master every proposition in the first two books of the *Principia*. He regarded the third book on the *System of the World* as most likely to prove profitable to the ordinary reader.

Although Newton had completed his draft of the first book of the *Principia* before the summer of 1685, it was not officially presented to the Royal Society until April 28, 1686. A committee was immediately appointed to attend to the printing of the book, and to consult with the author on all important details.

Everything was moving along smoothly—when suddenly a cloud appeared on the horizon. It was Hooke again!

Francis Aston, the secretary of the Society at the time and Newton's close friend, hurried to Halley with the new problem, the "human problem."

"Hooke has been complaining to members. He asserts that Newton got his main idea about gravity from him, Hooke. It's the one about gravity decreasing inversely as the square of the distance. What do you think of this strange claim, Mr. Halley?" Aston sounded irritated.

Halley smiled, "Hooke says that? Why, we all sort of

guessed the inverse square law—Wren and I and Hooke—and probably many others. But a surmise is not a mathematical proof. And that's what Newton contributed—the proof we were incapable of providing."

"I don't like it at all," growled Aston. "I don't like it. And furthermore, Hooke feels Newton is morally obligated to acknowledge in the *Principia* that he, Hooke, was the inventor of the inverse square law. Hooke hopes to ride to fame on Newton's coattails!"

"He wants that!" cried Halley, turning serious. "Perhaps I'd better inform Newton of Hooke's claim. It's going to disturb him and I wish I didn't have to bring it up. Newton detests this sort of bickering. It will destroy all of the pleasure in his work."

"But why tell Newton anything at all?"

"Because someone else will—and I'd rather he got it from me. I'll write to Newton and break the bad news gently."

When the author of the *Principia* received Halley's tactfully worded note, he exploded. So controversy, which he abhorred so deeply, was about to plague him again! Now he was practically being accused of stealing the inverse square law from Hooke! What a malicious claim! Why he, Newton, had not only grasped the idea but had used it in his calculation twenty years earlier at Woolesthorpe!

Others were aware of this law and had been for many years. It could easily be derived from Huygen's paper on circular motion. Wren and Halley had surmised it. Bullialdus and Borelli, on the Continent, were acquainted with it. And now the vain Hooke wanted the sole credit for inventing it!

Newton was perfectly willing to acknowledge that other men had independently hit upon the inverse square law. What infuriated him was not the petty matter of priority. It was the implication that he, Newton, had not discovered the law by himself, but had "borrowed" it from Hooke!

His integrity as a human being was of supreme importance to Isaac Newton. And when that was questioned, he would quickly change from an emotionless and abstracted scholar to a fierce and relentless antagonist. Fame, honors, public esteem were of minor importance to Newton throughout his lifetime; but personal honesty was sacred to him and any attack upon it was certain to rouse him to indignation and anger.

"Mathematicians that find out, settle and do all the business," he wrote to Halley bitterly, "must content themselves with being nothing but dry calculators and drudges; and another, that does nothing but pretend and grasp at all things, must carry away all the invention. . . ."

In this same communication to Halley, the indignant professor reviewed the history of the inverse square law and showed that Hooke's claims had no basis in fact. Newton cited old letters to prove that he had understood and applied this law long before Hooke had ever mentioned it. Finally, the irate Newton said flatly that, though he had planned three books for the *Principia*, it was now his wish to abandon the third! "Philosophy," wrote the angry scientist, "is such an impertinently litigious lady that I am no sooner come near her, but she gives me a warning."

The third book which Newton was threatening to withhold happened to be of special interest to Halley as an astronomer. A *Principia* without the section in which Newton proposed to apply the theorems of the first book to the solar system and comets—was unthinkable!

Greatly upset, Halley hastened to Cambridge to try to soothe Newton. He explained that Hooke had never made any formal claim in regard to the inverse square law. It all stemmed, said Halley, from the excitment of a coffeehouse discussion at which Hooke had let fly with a number of wild assertions. The Royal Society had taken no official notice of his remarks. Newton was wrong to have exaggerated the importance of statements made under such circumstances. . . .

Halley's manner and evident concern over the effect of the incident on the public reception of the *Principia* served to calm the furious Newton. The latter felt sorry for Halley, the innocent bystander who was most likely to be injured by the dispute. For by this time it had become evident that the Royal Society lacked funds with which to publish the *Principia.* It had recently spent a large sum of money on the printing of an elaborate work on fishes—which didn't sell as well as had been expected. As a result there was no money left for the *Principia,* a work generally regarded as a highly important but incomprehensible contribution to science.

Newton was aware of the situation and felt obligated to Halley, for the latter had generously offered to bring out the *Principia* at his own expense. He also suspected that the idealistic young astronomer, a man of moderate means, might have to get into debt in order to carry out the expensive printing project.

"It is all wild talk on the part of Hooke and should not be taken seriously," argued Halley. "You know Hooke and I know Hooke. The man is an excellent experimenter, but his imagination extends everywhere. That's why he tends to exaggerate his own accomplishments."

The older man remained silent for a few minutes. Actually, what Halley wanted most of all was a small thing—merely a line or two in the *Principia* to satisfy Hooke.

"It doesn't matter," Newton finally conceded. "Suppose I add the following statement to the fourth proposition: 'The inverse square law of gravity holds for all celestial bodies, as was discovered also independently by my countrymen Wren, Hooke and Halley.' "

Halley let out a sigh of relief. "It isn't true, but it is a grand gesture, Mr. Newton. I think you are very generous to make it. It will clear the air immediately."

Newton was pleased at his friend's joy. Since he felt so indebted to the genial Halley, it was a pleasure to be able to lighten the burden the latter had so altruistically assumed.

"You'll complete the third book, then, Mr. Newton?"

The Cambridge professor nodded. The Hooke affair was now a closed matter as far as he was concerned. What was important at the moment was to co-operate with Halley.

The *Principia* was published in the summer of 1687, and at once became an imperishable monument to Halley's faith in Newton, and love for science. The first edition sold out quickly, although the book was written in a style calculated to discourage the non-mathematical reader. The educated people of the time sensed in the *Principia* a work of immense importance—even though the reading of it involved intellectual labor of the severest kind.

Within ten years the *Principia* was being taught at Cambridge; in France, the followers of Descartes resisted Newtonian ideas for about twenty years. However, it was on the Continent, almost a century later, that great mathematicians like Laplace and Lagrange devoted their lives to completing and extending Newton's work. The final result was mechanics, the crowning glory, and the most exact and best organized branch of classical physics!

For two hundred years Newtonian ideas dominated all scientific thinking. It was not until the twentieth century that Einstein began to question the basic assumptions of classical mechanics. The result was a number of drastic theoretical changes in our ideas concerning space, time, matter and energy.

When applied to the extremely large or small, it was shown that the Newtonian system gave results which were highly approximate rather than exact. In short, a correction was necessary. However, our engineers, and physicists, in their day-to-day work with the practical problems of the earth, still rely on Newonian ideas just as if no challenge to their validity had ever appeared!

15

HALLEY'S COMET

Edmund Halley, the ardent student of astronomy and mathematics and physics, had for many years been intrigued by the problem of comets. To most of humanity, these mysterious visitors from outer space were still objects of dread; their appearance never failed to stir up tales of evil or misfortune to come—like disease, famine or war. To Halley, however, comets represented an age-old puzzle which no one as yet had been able to solve. They swept into our solar system, moved toward the sun at an enormous speed and were finally hurled away from that massive body.

"It's hard to understand," he remarked to the scholarly Wren, "how comets manage to become visible to us for a short time and then disappear—apparently forever."

Wren shook his head. "The comets we see may have been here before. But how can we tell one comet from another? The small fraction of the path we are able to observe from the earth is too short to help us identify a particular comet."

"The path of approach diverges from the path of departure—like the sides of a parabola," noted Halley. "And this makes it seem that comets can never return once they swing away from the sun."

"Yes," agreed Wren, "no one knows what brings them into our world and no one knows where they go after they are out of sight."

Edmund Halley was not the type of man to dismiss a problem merely because it was difficult. In his mind he kept seeing the brilliant nucleus or head of a comet, consisting of loose solid material surrounded by a brilliant fog or coma, and the tail, often millions of miles long, trailing from the head—and strangely enough always pointing away from the sun. Some pressure from the sun, acting like a wind, always seemed to blow the tail back from a comet's head!

A brilliant comet flashed into view in 1682, giving Halley his first opportunity to make a number of careful observations on his own. He kept track of the comet's path both before and after it reached a point at which it was closest to the sun.

"What do you make of it?" asked Wren, who had also been studying the progress of the same comet.

"The path is a curve whose sides diverge," said Halley wryly. "From the direction in which it was moving, I can't see how this comet can possibly return—ever."

"True," agreed Wren. "The sun appeared to fling it away with great force. And that leaves us with the conclusion that each comet reveals itself only once to the people of our earth."

"There have been hundreds—even thousands—of comets observed in the past," said Halley, shaking his head. "It doesn't seem possible that none of them ever came back for a return visit."

"The lawless comets, the lawless comets," murmured Wren. "All heavenly bodies are subject to law—except comets. Or does it seem so because we don't understand enough about these wanderers through space?"

When the manuscript of the third book of the *Principia* reached him, Halley studied the section on comets with breathless interest. Would Newton's work shed light on the baffling behavior of comets? The young astronomer read on slowly, weighing each word as if nothing in the world could be more important.

What's this! said Halley to himself. Newton regards comets as subject to the laws of gravity. Yes, just as much so as the planets in the solar system! He says that both planets and comets move in elliptical orbits. Only the path of a comet is an immense elongated ellipse stretching far out into space while that of a planet is a slightly flattened circle. . . .

Halley shook himself. He had too much respect for Newton's mind to dismiss the latter's ideas as impossible or as a mere guess. According to the *Principia* a comet moves over a closed orbit and will return to the vicinity of our sun after a certain period of time.

"How long before a comet returns to our solar system?" he asked Wren.

"Hundreds of years, I'd say," answered his friend. "Their paths are so long that it would take longer than a human lifetime for most comets to come back to where they had been previously observed."

"Newton may be right," murmured Halley, "but I wish I could prove that his ideas are correct. It's quite likely I will be dead before the comet we saw a few years ago comes back into view."

Wren nodded. "That's the sad fact about comets. No astronomer lives long enough to prove anything. He must record what he sees and then hope that some future astronomer, still unborn, will complete the task."

But Halley's mind refused to dismiss the problem. There must be a few comets which make a complete circuit in less than a hundred years, he said to himself. If so—then a solution to the problem might not be impossible. Suddenly a thought struck him. Take the comet of 1682, for example. Newton says it had been here before and would be observed again—after a certain number of years. Why not find out if it had been here before? Why not? he asked himself.

Halley was trembling with excitement. At last—a way of verifying Newton's ideas about the orbits of comets! All an energetic investigator had to do was to search through old books and records to find out if anyone had ever seen a comet exactly like the visitor of 1682!

He hurried to consult Newton about this ambitious project. The latter listened carefully and then meditated for several minutes over Halley's plan.

"It's worth trying, Mr. Halley, it's worth trying," he finally decided. "Much depends on the accuracy of the descriptions left by those who have observed the comets of the past. How will you recognize the comet of 1682 in the old manuscripts, Mr. Halley?"

"I'll use your method, Mr. Newton, the one you explained in the third book. Three recorded positions of a comet will fix its exact path around the sun."

The older man nodded. "It's a tremendous undertaking, Mr. Halley. However, it may be that you will succeed in proving that the comet of 1682 has been here before."

This was exactly what the earnest astronomer was hoping to hear. In Isaac Newton's opinion there was a chance for success! What more could any researcher ask?

Halley got to work without delay, and for the next twenty years devoted every spare hour to his beloved project. He examined old books and pored over dusty manuscripts, forever on the lookout for any mention of comets of the past. If fortunate enough to find the necessary information, he would immediately plot its path. The burning question was always this: Was the comet described in an old record the one he himself had observed in 1682?

It was no, no—and still no, after long years of patient searching. But the ardent Halley refused to be discouraged. Someday he would find an old comet whose description fitted the visitor of 1682—perfectly!

Finally it happened! And Halley experienced a thrill which repaid him amply for his many years of labor. He came across a description of a comet exactly like the one of 1682! It had been observed by Kepler and other astronomers in 1607.

The tireless Halley trembled with excitement when he made his great discovery. Subtracting 1607 from 1682, he found that seventy-five years must have elapsed between the two appearances of what he felt was exactly the same comet. Here was the first proof that Newton was right about comets; They obeyed the law of gravitation just as did the planets.

Newton beamed with pleasure when Halley burst into the former's study with the exciting news. He rejoiced in the triumph of his friend.

"I can't make my findings public for a long time," cried Halley. "After all, what I have is only a possibility—since the observations of the 1607 comet are not as reliable as those made in 1682."

"Still," noted Newton, "your job will be easier now. All you have to do is to continue your quest to comets reported seventy-five years before 1607."

"Yes," laughed Halley, "my task will be easier in one way and more difficult in another. I find that the further back I go the vaguer become the records of comets."

"It would be a master stroke, Mr. Halley," said the author of the *Principia*, "if you should finally establish that comets are regular visitors to our solar system. And I have a feeling that the glory of accomplishing this will be yours, Mr. Halley."

Warmed by Newton's confidence, Halley plunged once more into his researches. Years went by as he kept at his task with inexhaustible patience. He wanted to find still another record of a visit to the solar system by the same comet. Again his persistence was rewarded. In tracking down a description of a comet observed in 1531, he found that it bore a startling resemblance to the comets of 1607 and 1682!

But the 1531 comet had appeared seventy-six years before the one of 1607—not the seventy-five years Halley had expected. Near enough! said the happy astronomer to himself. Hadn't Newton stated that a comet might be slowed down as the result of passing very close to a distant planet?

Halley still refused to be hurried into a public announcement. He wanted to be absolutely certain that there was no flaw in his method or reasoning. What finally convinced him that all three appearances were of the same comet was a reference in still another ancient manuscript. It mentioned a comet seen in 1456. This was another seventy-five years back in time! And to cap it all, he came across a remark in historical work concerning a comet observed in 1305—giving a double period or one hundred fifty-one years!

Even Halley was now convinced, after twenty years of work, that the evidence was overwhelming. He published his findings, giving a detailed account of his investigation. At the same time, he ventured the audacious prediction that the very same comet would again appear seventy-five years from 1682. He set the date for the comet's return at the end of 1758, or the beginning of 1759. A slight delay, he explained, might be due to its passage close to the planet Jupiter.

At that time, such a prediction by a reputable astronomer was regarded as the height of foolhardiness. Suppose the comet did not appear as Halley predicted? He would then go down in scientific history as a vain blunderer. . . .

The crucial years were 1531, 1607, and 1682. Would the next visit be in 1758? Halley realized that he would not be alive to rejoice over victory or brood over failure. He liked to shut his eyes and imagine he could see "his" comet moving majestically on and on, past the outermost planets of our solar system and into the unknown space beyond.

Would it return in time to save his reputation? The cheerful astronomer was confident it would.

On Christmas night, 1758, sixteen years after Halley's death, a brilliant comet swept into view. Astronomers all over the world were on the lookout, and immediately named it "Halley's comet"!

Halley was thus proved right, as were the ideas of the author of the *Principia.* The idealistic astronomer thereby achieved his dearest wish—that the credit for the discovery of the first periodic comet should go to an Englishman.

Halley's comet has since made its appearance in accordance with its discoverer's timetable. It was seen in 1835 and again in 1910. At this very moment, the comet is moving unhurriedly through interstellar space and is expected to "arrive," or move into view of earth-bound observers, in 1986!

16

TROUBLE WITH JAMES II

In the spring of 1687 Cambridge University was in a state bordering on panic. James II was now King, having succeeded to the throne upon the death of his brother Charles II in 1685. It soon became apparent that the ruler, with characteristic Stuart obstinacy was planning to move against the University, long the citadel of English Protestantism. James II, a firm believer in absolute monarchy, was determined to force the return of the English people to the Roman Catholic faith.

The Catholic citizens scattered through England and living in amity with their Protestant neighbors were aghast at the folly of the King. It was plain to all except a few fanatics at the Court that James's stubbornness could only lead to a violent popular reaction. Since his plan would most certainly fail, it was feared that many innocent Catholics would be left to suffer for their King's stupidity.

But James II refused to listen to reason. Early in February, 1687, the University received a letter from the King commanding that one Father Alban Francis, a Benedictine monk, be admitted to the degree of Master of Arts. The customary oaths, the same communication directed, were to be dispensed with in the case of Father Francis—regardless of what the existing statutes might require.

A petition was hastily drawn up. In it the University officials pointed out that the granting of a degree without first administering the oaths of allegiance and supremacy was contrary to the statutes under which Cambridge University was founded.

The danger to the University was clear to all. A Master of Arts was privileged to vote in the Cambridge Senate, and hence had a voice in the government of the University. If the King could appoint one Roman Catholic, he could appoint many; and it would thus be possible for his appointees to change the Protestant character of Cambridge, from which had come many of the bishops and archbishops of the Church of England.

James paid no attention to the protesting petition, which had been signed by all but two or three Fellows of the University. Instead, a few weeks later, he sent another letter repeating his command in regard to Father Francis—along with veiled threats of punitive measures should this second order go unheeded.

The answer of the Cambridge Senate was another communication to the King, in which the University's refusal to obey the royal mandate was defended in detail by citing law and precedent. Unless Father Francis was willing to take the oaths of allegiance and supremacy, there was no legal way whereby the University could confer the Master of Arts degree upon him. This answer amounted to a polite "No" to the king; for these oaths, whose very purpose was to protect the Church of England from change, could obviously not be taken by a Roman Catholic.

The University was defying the King! James II, furious at this challenge to his authority, became more than ever determined to teach Cambridge University a lesson. After a few weeks of silence, he struck hard. "The Vice-Chancellor in person, and the Senate by themselves and their deputies" were summoned to appear before the High Court of Ecclesiastical Commissioners to answer to charges of contempt!

Eight delegates, of whom Isaac Newton was one, were elected to represent the Cambridge Senate and to accompany Dr. John Pechell, the Vice-Chancellor, to London. A few days before leaving, the entire group met to prepare its case against the admission of Father Francis.

The argument of the University was put into proper legal form. There was little fire or fight in evidence among the timid scholars as they sat at the conference table. Every man present was thinking of the dreaded Jeffreys, the most feared and hated judge in England, who presided over the High Court. None of them looked forward to appearing before this infamous character, whose unbridled tongue, viciousness and cruelty were detested and feared throughout the land.

Perhaps the only delegate who remained innocent of any fear was Isaac Newton. He had only recently completed his monumental *Principia* and was still too far removed from the practical world to worry about ferocious, drunken judges.

Stanhope, the Chancellor of Ely, began to speak of the dangers and difficulties of the situation in which the University found itself.

"We are going to be called bigoted, intolerant and illogical," he declared. "Our position isn't strong in this Father Francis case, not strong at all."

Dr. Pechell, a timid man by nature, looked alarmed. "What do you mean, sir?"

Stanhope shrugged his shoulders. "We have obeyed royal

mandates before. The opposition can cite dozens of instances where Master of Arts degrees were granted at royal commands. The University honored earlier mandates from Charles I, Cromwell, Charles II and even the present King. Why quibble over this particular one?"

"But this one is different," spoke up Mr. Finch, one of the delegates.

"How so?" asked Stanhope frowning.

"Because this candidate refuses to take the oaths."

Stanhope eyed the objector pityingly. "The High Court will argue that only lately Cambridge granted the Master of Arts degree to a Mohammedan. Then why not to a Christian?"

"That argument is not valid, sir," said Newton from his place at the end of the table.

All eyes turned toward the famous author of the *Principia*. Newton seldom spoke out at meetings, and when he did it was always briefly and to the point.

"The case of the Mohammedan is of an altogether different nature," he began slowly. "The customary oaths were dispensed with because an honorary degree does not entitle an individual to a vote in the Senate of the University."

That was all. Newton's remark went right to the heart of the matter, and most of the Fellows around the long oak table nodded agreement.

Stanhope, however, remained fearful of the King's wrath. Why not, this once, admit Father Francis to the degree without oaths? he argued. A single Catholic vote in the Senate would certainly not endanger the Church of England! At the same time it would save the University from unpleasantness or even worse—since the full fury of the King's wrath was bound to fall upon Cambridge. Would it not be wise to admit Father Francis as commanded—but with the proviso that such action must not be regarded as a precedent?

The delegates were tempted to compromise. It did seem a simple way out of a dangerous conflict with the Crown. Why not? As long as no precedent was established, what was the harm?

While the other delegates were discussing Stanhope's suggestion, Newton got up from the table and began to pace the length of the room. He could hear his colleagues. . . . Why fight and get mauled when it wasn't necessary? Admit Father Francis without oaths and get rid of the entire problem. . . .

Stanhope smiled and began to write out his compromise on a long sheet of parchment. He was pleased that the unworldly Fellows had finally seen the light.

Suddenly Newton slipped back to his place at the table and remained standing, lost in thought, while his fellow delegates waited for him to speak. "This is giving up the question, gentlemen, this is giving up the question," he said, shaking his head sternly.

"What would you have us do, Mr. Newton?" asked Stanhope scornfully. What did this mathematically gifted recluse know about the world? he said to himself.

"I think it would be better to wait until we get a legal opinion on this compromise," said Newton quietly. "I do not think it will stand up in court. The King could still continue to order the University to confer degrees on whomever he pleased—regardless of what we may say about precedent."

"What would you have us do—refuse to compromise?" remarked Stanhope coldly.

"I think it best not to yield on this matter," answered Newton firmly. "If we submit in the Father Francis case, we shall have lost all. It means opening the door to a flood of similar mandates. Gentlemen, we have law, precedent and public opinion on our side. To surrender when in a strong position is foolish."

Immediately a heated discussion broke out on the merits of each course of action; finally, Mr. Finch declared that he agreed with Newton. Other Fellows also threw their support to the latter. It soon appeared that the author of the *Principia* had succeeded in winning the majority of the delegates to a "no compromise" stand!

Before long the fateful day arrived. On April 21, 1687, the Vice-Chancellor of Cambridge University and eight distinguished scholars—among whom was Isaac Newton—appeared before the Lord Commissioners in the Council Chambers.

There sat Lord Jeffreys, glaring balefully at poor Dr. Pechell, the Vice-Chancellor. The room was crowded with spectators, for the case had aroused widespread interest. Even the staunchest supporters of the Stuart monarchy were horrified at what the reckless King was attempting to do. To the English people, Cambridge and Oxford were the bulwarks of their Protestantism; and the attack upon the religious foundations of these institutions struck a rebellious chord even among those whose loyalty to the Stuarts had never been questioned.

The University had an excellent case; the law was entirely on its side. The granting of degrees without oaths had always been confined to the honorary type. No right to participate in the government of the University had ever been conferred by such degrees. The University, in its long history, had invariably refused to grant degrees without oaths under circumstances similar to those of the Father Francis mandate. And previous governments had never failed to cancel such commands when Cambridge University objected to carrying them out.

But law or precedent meant nothing to Lord Jeffreys—long accustomed to riding roughshod over the rights of those who opposed him. He eyed the frightened Dr. Pechell vindictively for a few moments.

"So you are the Vice-Chancellor of Cambridge University?" sneered Jeffreys.

"Yes, my Lord," answered Dr. Pechell in a trembling voice.

"And you have the insolence to come here with your foolish reasons for refusing to obey your King? How can you stand there mumbling laws and precedents when your King makes a simple request of the University?"

There was no answer from poor Pechell.

"Why, Father Francis has more understanding in his little finger," thundered Jeffreys, "than exists in the brainless heads of all of you divines put together!"

There was still no answer, for the delegates knew about Jeffreys and his almost insane violence. Very wisely, they held their peace in spite of the tongue-lashing.

"We cannot disobey the laws under which the University was founded," began Dr. Pechell waveringly after a long pause. "Before a degree may be granted to Father Francis, he must take the oaths of supremacy and—"

"Bah!" interrupted Jeffreys. "Oaths, oaths! What nonsense! What do you know about oaths, sir? You are Vice-Chancellor, and you had to take an oath on being inducted into that office, did you not?"

"Yes, Lord Jeffreys, I—I did."

"What a waste that oath was in your case!" roared the Judge. "You cannot even remember that you owe your exalted position to the Crown." Suddenly a thin sneer flashed over Jeffrey's bloated face. "What oath did you take, sir? I want to hear it from your own lips, Honorable Vice-Chancellor!"

Every eye in the packed chamber was now fixed on the unfortunate Dr. Pechell, whose face began to twitch with fear and nervousness. He was frightened at the thought that he might not remember his own oath of office. And because he was so frightened, the poor man simply couldn't remember it!

There stood the Vice-Chancellor, openmouthed and sweating with embarrassment, trying hopelessly to get the words out. No one in the packed room laughed, for the majority of spectators felt sorry for the disorganized scholar. Even some of Jeffrey's fellow Commissioners felt that he was being unnecessarily cruel to poor Dr. Pechell.

Finally one of the Cambridge delegates could stand the sorry spectacle no longer. Throwing caution to the winds, he decided that the Vice-Chancellor simply had to be helped out of this degrading predicament.

"May I recite the oath which Dr. Pechell is too upset to deliver, Lord Jeffreys?" began the brave soul.

The angry Judge eyed the speaker contemptuously. "Who are you? Are you Vice-Chancellor?" he demanded.

"No—but—your Lordship—"

"You are not Vice-Chancellor?" persisted Jeffreys.

"No—I am not—but—"

"You, my good Doctor, are not Vice-Chancellor!" roared Jeffreys. "When you are, you may speak. Till then it will become you to hold your peace."

After this last outburst, the Commissioners retired to confer briefly; in a short time, Jeffreys emerged with the sentence of the Court: Because of disobedience and contempt, Dr. John Pechell was to be deprived of his Vice-Chancellorship and suspended from the Mastership of his college.

Jeffreys was certain that this drastic punishment would quickly bring the obviously timid Cambridge delegation into line. Now that they had lost their leader, the confused Fellows would meekly accede to the King's wishes, thought the crafty Judge.

However, Jeffreys had reckoned without the stubborn courage of the aroused Cambridge scholars, who were furious at the summary manner in which their Vice-Chancellor had been treated. The result was that the group promptly resolved that, without Dr. Pechell at its head, the delegation no longer felt it truly represented Cambridge University.

"Let us state our position in writing," suggested Newton, "since it is impossible to speak without interruption before this Court."

The majority agreed, and a statement was drawn up for presentation to the Lord High Commissioner. It again summed up the case for the University; it answered Jeffreys' argument and showed that in refusing to obey the King the University was simply obeying the laws under which it had been established.

At the next meeting of the Court, the delegates laid their written argument before Jeffreys. The latter glanced scornfully at the document and immediately threw it aside contemptuously. Things were not going as well as the presiding Judge had expected. He was well aware that the position of the University was strong, legally. However, Jeffreys had counted on terrifying the scholars into submission by threats and insults.

"I am not interested in what you may write or assert," he exclaimed in a voice choking with fury. He glared at each of the delegates and then added, "Gentlemen, the best way will be a ready obedience to His Majesty's commands for the future and, by giving a good example to others, to make amends for the poor example given you."

Jeffreys cleared his throat and smiled at the silent scholars in a nasty, superior way. "As for you, most of you are divines. I will therefore send you home with a text from the Scriptures: 'Go your way and sin no more lest a worse thing happen to you.' "

Cambridge had won out against the King—and Jeffreys!

There was much rejoicing throughout the land over the fact that the University had not been frightened into submission. Even the King now began to be alarmed by the violent public opposition to his foolish schemes. Englishmen might give way in many things out of loyalty to the Crown, but an attack on their Universities was regarded as endangering fundamental English liberties.

Before long, James II abandoned the entire plan. Oxford was in a state of revolt; a regiment of dragoons had to be quartered there to prevent outbreaks by rebellious students. Cambridge had shown that the King's command could be safely ignored. James's more moderate advisers kept urging caution. . . .

But it was too late! After having alienated almost every social and religious group in England, the King's attack upon the Universities was regarded as the last straw: it lost him the support of even the die-hards among the nobility. It became clear to almost everyone that James II had to go! A peaceful revolution was contemplated, and negotiations with William of Orange were begun with the full approval of the majority of Englishmen. Three years of James II was all England could stand!

In 1689, Cambridge University, impressed by Isaac Newton's stubborn courage in the Father Francis affair, elected the famed author of the *Principia* to Parliament. It was a most radical change for the meditative, self-effacing mathematician and scientist. After twenty-five years spent in grappling with ideas in cloistered Cambridge, Newton was about to enter a glittering arena where he would rub shoulders with politicians and courtiers.

17

RESTLESS YEARS

Isaac Newton took no active part in the Convention Parliament, whose main business was to legitimatize the position of William of Orange as King of England. Contrary to the predictions of his friends, the Cambridge professor, after long years of blessed solitude in library and laboratory, found the feverish activity of London immensely appealing. The reaction of the forty-seven-year-old Newton was like that of a country youth being shown the sights of a big city for the first time.

As a Member of Parliament, Newton took the opportunity to renew his friendship with Charles Montagu, an ambitious young man who had become one of the leaders of the Whig party. Through the latter, the author of the *Principia* was introduced to John Locke, the famous philosopher, Richard Bentley, the well-known theologian, Samuel Pepys, the diarist, and other prominent people. The friendship between Newton and the brilliant, witty Montagu dated from about 1679, when the latter was an undergraduate at Trinity College.

"How do you like living in London?" asked Montagu at the end of the first Parliamentary session.

Newton eyed the younger man gravely. "It is different—

exciting. I think I should like to stay in London permanently."

Montagu laughed. "But there is no tranquillity here, at least not the kind one finds at Trinity. London is no place for a thinker. Only ambitious men—whose eagerness to get ahead exceeds their understanding—belong in London."

Newton shook his head in disagreement. "I like it, Charles, I like it. There is a feeling of life here, and that is what appeals to me."

What Newton was seeking so eagerly at this stage in his life was *change!* The seventeen months of superhuman concentration on the *Principia* had left his mind in a state of exhaustion. And his body was almost as weary as his brain. It was the price he paid for presenting the world with that tremendous work.

Only after he had completed the *Principia* did Newton begin to breathe freely again. For relaxation he had immediately turned to chemistry and theology. Subconsciously, however, he was troubled by a fear, a fear that his creative life was over! He was aware that his brain was no longer as creative as it had been; for one thing, it now tended to slip away from problems he would feed it—instead of working at them smoothly and steadily as before.

Was his mind worn out? he wondered. Would a rest bring back its vigor and productiveness? Or had it been permanently weakened as the result of having been overused or forced for so many years?

Isaac Newton was frightened. Suppose, as was quite possible, the creative period of his life was definitely over. He was not yet fifty years old. What could he look forward to? Unless his mind continued to be productive of ideas, there would be scant pleasure in living out his life at Trinity as a Lucasian professor. In short, Newton was afraid of the future and had therefore convinced himself that living in London would solve all of his problems.

Up to now, it was as if Newton had been content to sit at the edge of a quiet pool, protected by massive rocks from the mainstream rushing by a few feet away. Let others be carried along by the fast-running water! He, Isaac Newton, could find pleasure and contentment in seeking answers to questions which the impatient mainstreamers were too busy to care about.

But now everything seemed changed. He was tired—and for the first time felt that life was passing him by. He had sat by himself long enough; now he wanted desperately to fling himself into the current which would carry him, as it did most of humanity, swiftly and smoothly through the years ahead.

After a few months, during which Newton had attended Parliamentary sessions faithfully, he began to stay away for days at a time.

"Have you been ill?" Montagu asked one morning.

"I've just returned from Woolesthorpe," explained Newton in a lifeless voice. "My mother is down with malignant fever. It seems serious and she is suffering intensely."

"I'm sorry. I had no idea she wasn't well."

"My half brother had the same sickness, and my mother must have contracted it while nursing him back to health," explained Newton, looking almost beside himself with worry.

Again and again he would rush home to take care of his pain-racked mother. He would sit up with her day and night, applying dressings and ointments and handling her as deftly and lovingly as if she were a child. But it was of no avail; in spite of the ministrations of her son and the advice of the best doctors, Hannah Smith died.

Newton was more attached to his mother than to any other

person in the world; her loss left a scar which took years to heal. He needed her, for the love and quiet understanding which existed between them had served to balance his overpowering absorption in ideas.

He returned to London more disturbed and discontented than ever, now that the single emotional tie which bound him to another soul had been severed. The need for change now seemed a thousand times more pressing!

Though he delivered no speeches before the Convention Parliament, his fellow Whigs were proud to have the distinguished Cambridge scholar as a member of their party. To him was assigned the important job of gaining the support of the Universities for the new King William III. Many scholars at Cambridge and Oxford felt that the ousting of James II had been an illegal act. Newton's eminent position in the academic world, plus the logic of his arguments, succeeded in convincing most of the hesitant University men that they owed their allegiance to the new King.

In 1690, after having been in session for thirteen months, the Convention Parliament was dissolved and Newton prepared to return to Cambridge. Montagu, aware of the restlessness of his friend, tried to comfort him.

"You have many friends here, Mr. Newton. We are scouring the government departments to find a good place for you. The Whig party appreciates your loyalty and efforts. Rest assured that our gratitude will be shown in a tangible way before very long, Mr. Newton."

"Thank you, Charles. People have been very kind to me in London."

Montagu eyed his friend thoughtfully for a few seconds. "Are you sure you will be happy in London? Are you really prepared to give up Cambridge for the metropolis?"

"I am sure, Charles," answered Newton, looking off into the

distance. "I imagine that I'll be happier here—for a while. At any rate, I'd like to try." He meditated for several seconds and added, "The change might help."

Montagu was an understanding man. He wished he could do something for his distinguished friend. The death of his mother was what had upset the scholarly Newton, he said to himself. Isaac Newton's accomplishments were the glory of English science. Was it not time for the nation to do something for him?

After getting settled in Cambridge again, Newton threw himself into theological studies. He undertook an exhaustive analysis of certain significant passages in the New Testament. The result of his researches was an important contribution entitled *Two Notable Corruptions of the Scripture.*

A year passed and still no news from his friends about that all-important government post in London. He knew that Montagu, Pepys, Locke, Lord and Lady Monmouth and others had not forgotten him. Nevertheless, the tired Newton became more and more impatient, with the result that his tension and nervousness increased.

To occupy his mind, he returned to his studies of the lunar theory. He also worked in his laboratory and discovered the famous law of cooling: the heat lost by radiation and convection by one body to another is proportional to the temperature difference between the two.

At about the same time, his experiments turned up an important fact: solids melt and liquids boil at constant temperatures. Newton immediately applied his discovery to the problem of marking off or graduating thermometers. All one had to do was to place the bulb of an unmarked thermometer in melting ice and then in boiling water. The distance on the thermometer tube between the two marks—the freezing point and boiling point of water—could then be divided into equal parts or degrees. Thus all thermometers marked off by his method would be comparable!

By the end of 1692, the strain under which Newton had been living revealed itself in the form of a nervous breakdown. He began to brood over his failure to obtain the promised position in London. The Cambridge professor could think of little else, so fixed had become his notion that life in London would cure his restlessness!

He began to suffer from insomnia over long periods, until he was almost beside himself for lack of sleep. Newton's mind took to magnifying petty irritations. Here he was begging for a position like a typical fawning job hunter. His friends' concern was only a pretense. Once out of sight, he had been quickly forgotten by them. . . .

It was galling to an independent soul like Newton to have to ask favors from "important" personages. Indeed, the world seemed bent upon ignoring his existence. All in all, Newton managed to work himself into an extraordinary state of unreasonableness during this period of nervous and physical exhaustion. The unhappy mathematician, worn out by lack of sleep, even ventured to write to some of his friends. Without mincing words he accused them of insincerity and declared he would have nothing to do with them in the future!

He had other troubles. His dog Diamond upset a lighted candle in Newton's study. Before the fire could be brought under control, important papers on which he had labored for many years had gone up in flames. The effect on the distraught professor of the loss of his precious notes on optics and chemistry may well be imagined. With this final blow, his spirits sank to a new low.

Pepys and Locke had each received an incomprehensible letter from Newton at about this time. Very much disturbed, the two men hastened to confer about the health and difficulties of their mutual friend.

"We must do something to help him!" exclaimed Locke. "It is plain that Newton is not well."

"What can we do? From what he wrote, I don't think Newton wants to see either of us again." Pepys looked distressed. "That such nonsense should come from a man like Isaac Newton is sad, very sad," he added.

"It will pass, I am sure," comforted Locke. "Do you suppose he feels as he does because his appointment as Provost of King's College was turned down? We explained that it was because he wasn't in priest's orders. Still, he may feel that we neglected to push his candidacy with sufficient energy."

"But we did all we could!" cried Pepys. "The King and Council were ready to make him Provost—until it was pointed out that such action would be contrary to law." He shook his head gravely and added, "We must help him. There have been few Newtons in the world, and England may never be blessed with another like him."

Locke was silent for a few seconds. "If we could only ask someone at Cambridge to drop in to see Newton—and perhaps through conversation find out the root of our friend's trouble—"

Pepys jumped to his feet excitedly. "A capital idea! And I know just the right person for this errand—a kindly, understanding soul. He is John Millington of Magdalene College. I'll write to him at once."

True to his word, Pepys communicated with Millington, explained the problem and asked him to pay Newton a visit. Millington hastened to comply, and soon sent a reassuring letter to Pepys. It was true that Newton was still in a slightly melancholy frame of mind. However, he was recovering from a nervous attack during which he had been unable to sleep for days at a time. Also Newton had expressed keen regret at having written irrational letters to his friends at a time when he was sick, feverish. . . . And finally, Millington himself ventured the opinion that it was a national disgrace for a man of Newton's genius to be so neglected by those in power.

Newton's friends were relieved! According to Millington, there was every hope that the Cambridge mathematician would soon be himself again. The former had indirectly pointed out the root of Newton's difficulty—his failure to obtain that much-desired position in London. So Locke, Pepys, Montagu and others resolved to redouble their efforts on behalf of the famed author of the *Principia.*

Within a few months, Newton had completely recovered, thanks to a basically sound constitution. He apologized to his friends for the letters he had written when under great stress, and his explanations were graciously accepted.

As his strength returned, Newton's mind became creative again. He turned once more to the puzzling problem of the moon's motions, and began to collect astronomical data for his lunar theory. At the same time, he corresponded at length with Bentley on theological matters. And finally, at the urgings of his friends, he got started on corrections and additions for the projected second edition of the *Principia.*

In the meantime, Charles Montagu, with the Whigs back in power, had been appointed to the important post of Chancellor of the Exchequer. Newton's friends were jubilant.

"With Montagu and Somers so high in the government," cried Pepys when he brought the good news to Locke, "it is only a matter of time before a desirable place is found for Isaac Newton."

"I hope so," said John Locke fervently. "No man in England is more deserving. And Newton is asking for only a small thing, but to him it is of vital importance. If he gets that position in London, he'll probably never again feel that his contributions have been ignored by the nation."

Charles Montagu did not forget his old friend. Before long, Newton was called to London to confer with Somers, Locke and the new Chancellor of the Exchequer. The subject for discussion was the disease which had long afflicted English commerce—the debasement of the silver currency.

Soon rumors began to fly through London that Isaac Newton was slated for an excellent post in the Mint. This Newton at first denied, for no such place had been formally offered him, and the possibility of disappointment loomed large.

On March 19, 1696, all difficulties having been cleared away, Newton received a note from Montagu: the King had promised to make the Cambridge mathematician the new Warden of the Mint, the present Warden having been promoted to Commissioner of Customs! The salary would be five or six hundred pounds a year; and the duties as Warden, according to Montagu, would not be burdensome.

"I am glad," wrote the Chancellor of the Exchequer, "that at last I can give a good proof of my friendship—and the esteem the King has of your merits."

Newton was overjoyed! The thought of living in London stirred up a new interest in life. At fifty-four, a different and exciting form of existence beckoned to the tired author of the *Principia*, and he looked forward eagerly to the kind of routine the average man likes to complain about!

Like a tree which has been producing magnificent fruit in abundance for many years, Isaac Newton's mind needed rest. . . .

18

WARDEN OF THE MINT

Charles Montagu, the brilliant young Chancellor of the Exchequer who later became Lord of Halifax, was planning many long-needed reforms of the financial system of England. He aimed to make the Bank of England the core institution of a national banking system; among other advantages this would make it easier to raise the large sums needed for carrying on the wars with France.

But before he could proceed to long-term reforms, Montagu first had to solve the most pressing and immediate problem of all—the restoration of the currency. The circulation of debased silver coins had long been a festering sore on the business life of England.

"We must do something about the miserable clipped coins which have been circulating for hundreds of years," he explained to Newton. "How can trade be carried on efficiently when the passage of money between buyer and seller, or between employer and laborer, is invariably accompanied by bitter outcries and arguments? Englishmen feel they are being cheated when paid in debased coin—which is practically always."

Montagu was referring to the clipping or filing of silver coins, for many years a widely practiced and profitable fraud. Most of the coins then in circulation had been minted generations ago by the crudest of methods. Shears were once used to cut the disks out of large silver sheets; the edges of the coins were not milled and there was no inscription along the rims to make tampering easy to detect. The result was that the coins were not exactly round, and the weight of silver in each, even when new, was almost always a little more or a little less than the legal standard.

As might be expected under such conditions, there were few unmutilated coins in circulation. Unscrupulous individuals could not resist a quick and fairly safe way of making money: paring a sliver from this coin, or filing the thicker section of that one, soon added up to a neat bit of silver which could be melted down and sold.

For many years hanging was made the penalty both for counterfeiting and for clipping coins. But even that did not put an end to the practice, for no matter how many offenders were sent to the gallows, the currency continued to be debased. It got to the point where juries refused to convict occasional coin clippers. The practice had become so widespread that the public no longer regarded it as a serious crime!

"I don't suppose it would help to mint large quantities of improved coins and throw them into the market places," observed Newton.

The younger man shook his head vigorously. "It's been tried again and again for over fifty years but to no avail. We've turned out fifteen thousand pounds per week of beautifully minted, tamperproof coins with a legend close to the milled edges—and what happened? They disappeared as though they were in a bottomless pit! Within two days not a single new coin could be found anywhere in the land! Whoever acquired one hastened to hoard it for its superior weight and value. No, that solution has been tried and it won't work. It's the old story: bad coins drive out the good."

"It seems an impossible situation about which little can be done—unless we start afresh by discarding all the old coins," said Newton thoughtfully. "But would it be practical to try and provide the nation with an entirely new supply of silver money?"

"That is exactly what I proposed to do!" cried Montagu. "It is the only solution to our problem. Things simply can't go on as at present. Why—take any hundred silver coins at random and weigh them. I warrant that their total weight will be half of what it should be legally! We can pass laws and laws to help the nation, but I doubt whether any single reform will benefit England as much as a system of honest currency!"

"How can we get the mutilated coins back to the Mint for melting and recoining?" asked Newton. "The people need silver currency in their everyday business transactions. They won't like doing without while waiting for the freshly minted coins to appear."

"It must be done," insisted Montagu earnestly. "And anyone who helps bring it about quickly and efficiently will be performing an invaluable service to the English people. Nothing is more important—nothing!"

With that, the new Chancellor acquainted Newton with the details of the recoinage measure which the King was about to approve. The government would bear the loss involved in the exchange of the clipped coins for new and perfect ones. . . . A date would be set after which no debased coins could be used except for the payment of taxes. . . . And finally, after a certain day the acceptance of mutilated currency in trade would be forbidden by law.

"The success of the plan depends entirely upon the efficiency of the Mint. We must pour not a mere fifteen thousand pounds of new coins into the market each week—but two, even three times that amount. The greater the production of the Mint, the less will be the dislocation caused by the temporary scarcity of money. We need your help, Mr. Newton."

"I'll do my utmost," promised the older man. "I'll drop what I've been working on and try to be of service to the nation."

"You'll occupy the key position," continued Montagu. "In the months ahead there will be charges of favoritism. The individuals who manage to get hold of the new money first will reap advantages in trade. Fortunately, the name Isaac Newton means something in England. We need you because every Englishman has the greatest confidence in your integrity and ability."

As it turned out, the selection of Isaac Newton as the chief Mint executive during this trying period proved a stroke of genius! The post of Warden of the Mint up to then had been regarded as a well-paying job with few responsibilities; it was the perfect sinecure for a political favorite. Montagu knew that the recoinage project would fail miserably—with disastrous results to the nation—if the wrong man was appointed Warden. Also, the rest of the reforms he had in mind would be laughed out of Parliament if recoinage proved a fiasco!

The new Warden of the Mint quickly applied himself to his job with the vigor and tenacity which had characterized his academic life. Ten new furnaces were hastily constructed behind the Treasury; and before long the melting down of the old, hand-hammered coins, the casting of silver into ingots and the minting of new money were proceeding full blast.

Newton found it necessary to establish branch mints in towns near London in order to increase production still more. For the sake of efficiency he asked several of his fellow scientists to act as his representatives in these smaller mints.

"I need someone I can trust," he said to Halley. "According to Montagu, the political enemies of recoinage will stop at nothing to make the undertaking a failure. I wish you would see your way clear to act as supervisor of the mint at Chester."

Halley accepted the job as a patriotic duty, as did several others whom Newton approached. It was well that the Warden of the Mint had the foresight to place trusted men in key positions. Before long, his supervisors ran into the usual difficulties with the old-line bureaucrats who were either too lazy or too stubborn to push the minting of coins at the rate set by Newton. In addition, the political opponents of the Whigs did not hesitate to resort to devious measures in their efforts to slow down the recoinage process. Certain individuals went so far as to attempt to stir up discontent in a few of the smaller mints. And to cap it all, cries of corruption, inefficiency and bribery in regard to the operation of the Mint were repeatedly raised!

But Isaac Newton would not be deflected from his goal—the minting of more and more currency each day. The weekly output of silver coins rose from the previous high of fifteen thousand pounds per week to thirty thousand, then to sixty thousand, finally to one hundred and twenty thousand pounds!

Montagu was jubilant. It now appeared that the difficult change from old to new coins was going to take place without disorganizing trade.

"Wonderful!" he exclaimed, pumping the Warden's hand. "A magnificent accomplishment! England will long remember you for it, Mr. Newton."

"We've had trouble at some of the small mints," said the

Warden, looking worried. "Weddell was challenged to a duel by one of the old officials, and some of my men have been threatened with physical violence. Halley wants to resign, but I'm hoping that he'll change his mind and stay on a while longer."

Montagu shrugged off these minor difficulties. "Our opponents are trying desperately to make recoinage a failure. But I don't think they can do it. We're getting to the crucial period now. If we manage to keep afloat the next few weeks, it will be clear sailing afterward. Things will be tight, very tight, for a short time. However, with your mints turning out miraculous numbers of coins, I'm confident we'll pull through the crisis."

During March and April of 1696, there were no signs of panic in the market places of England. The people had gotten used to the idea of recoinage, and there was still no scarcity of coins. Saturday, May 2, was the last day on which the government would accept clipped silver currency for the payment of taxes. Beginning the following Monday, May 4, no mutilated money at all could legally pass anywhere in the land.

Then the real trouble began! There were not enough unclipped old coins in circulation for everyday business transactions. And there were as yet too few freshly minted coins to fill the void left by the removal of the mutilated currency!

Montagu and other Whig leaders held their breath. The situation could easily lead to riots in the cities and turmoil in the trade centers. Fortunately, the English people remained calm and patient during the temporary shortage; many turned to devices like promissory notes and barter to tide them over.

By August, 1696, there was a marked improvement in currency conditions. Newton and his aides were pouring so much money into the markets that it soon became evident that the stringency was definitely over. After that, both the Warden and the Chancellor of the Exchequer relaxed; and by 1699, the entire recoinage project had been successfully completed.

All through those hectic years, Newton never allowed himself to be disturbed by the wild charges leveled against him and his associates. He kept right on minting coins and shipping them to the cities and towns of the nation.

On a few occasions during the shortage period, the Warden of the Mint was offered bribes for "favors." It was a time when the acceptance of "gifts" by government officials was far from uncommon.

Once the agent of a socially prominent lady insisted on pressing a "gift" of six thousand pounds on Newton in connection with a special request for an allotment of new coins. The Warden indignantly refused the proffered money.

"But there is no dishonesty in one's accepting a small token of esteem," argued the agent.

"I'll have nothing to do with it," cried Newton angrily. "This is a bribe no matter what you may choose to call it."

The man shook his head sadly. "It is unfortunate, sir, that you do not know your own interest. As it happens, I represent one of the great ladies of London. And my employer is in a position to exert an exceedingly powerful influence—politically." He paused to allow the full significance of his remark to sink in.

The implied threat was too much for Newton. "I desire you to tell the lady," he thundered, as he rushed to the door of his office and flung it open, "that if she were here herself, and made me this offer, I would have desired her to get out of my house; and so I desire you, or you will be turned out!"

While recoinage was progressing, Newton put in long hours at the Mint, resolutely refusing to be drawn into scientific studies. It was the King's business and nothing else that occupied him during those busy years, and he would not be diverted.

However, that extraordinary mathematical ability was still there. One afternoon, after a particularly trying day at the Mint, Newton found an interesting communication from the Royal Society awaiting him at his home. It seemed that John Bernoulli, famed Swiss mathematician, had challenged the world to solve two unusually difficult problems:

1. To find the curve connecting two points, at different heights and not in the same vertical line, along which a body, acted upon only by gravity, will fall in the shortest time.
2. To find the curve, having this property, so that two segments of a straight line, drawn through the curve from any given point, will, when raised to any given power and added together, make the same sum.

Bernoulli, who had set up these problems as a way of testing the ability of the world's leading mathematicians, planned to allow six months for their solution. However, at the request of his friend Leibnitz, who had succeeded in solving one of the problems, the challenger granted an additional year for the task.

Isaac Newton received the problems at about 4:00 P. M. Unable to resist a "puzzle," he concentrated on them through the night and into the morning. By 4:00 A. M. his solutions to both problems were ready to be dispatched to the Royal Society!

Newton's solutions were published anonymously in the *Transactions* of January, 1697, and read before the Society a month later. Bernoulli is said to have guessed the author's identity from the power and originality of the methods used.

"Tanquam ex ungue leonem!" the Swiss mathematician exclaimed. Even as the lion is known by his paw!

19

SHAPE OF THE EARTH

The next few years brought peace and contentment to Isaac Newton. Now that recoinage had been accomplished, largely due to his efforts, the Warden of the Mint felt he could relax. In 1699, Newton was promoted to Master of the Mint, a position he retained to the end of his life.

He enjoyed his house in Jermyn Street and soon brought into it his favorite niece Catherine Barton. The gay young lady, whose beauty and wit made her a favorite of London society, acted as housekeeper for her illustrious uncle for twenty years.

Newton was almost sixty years old at the beginning of the century. After long solitary years at Cambridge, he found comfort and pleasure in the warmth of public esteem. He was respected—almost to the point of reverence—by the leading men of his time. Renowned scientists from all over the world made their way to Jermyn Street to pay their respects to the author of the great *Principia*.

Catherine Barton, whom Newton adored, supplied the

gaiety at the gatherings of scientists and philosophers. But the charming Catherine was not content with entertaining sober-minded scholars; she soon established her own circle of gallants, poets and socialites—being careful not to mix her admirers with those of her famed uncle.

Except for occasional dinner parties, Newton continued to live simply; his habits remained unchanged as far as eating and studying were concerned. He would still forget meals during periods of absorption in ideas. And he would still insist on studying and writing far into the early morning hours.

It was about this time that the story of Dr. Stukeley's interesting experience began to be whispered about in London.

It seemed that the doctor had called on Newton one evening to discuss some matters pertaining to the Royal Society. On being ushered into the dining room by the servant, the visitor found much to his surprise that there was no one there to greet him.

Dr. Stukeley sat down, expecting his friend to appear at any moment. After all, this meeting had been arranged weeks before. And the servant had acted as if the caller were expected. An hour passed, then another hour—and still no Newton! The doctor was becoming more and more restless—and hungry. He noted with considerable interest that dinner had been set out for England's famed mathematician.

After heroically resisting temptation and hunger pangs for a while longer, the famished doctor finally gave up the struggle. He approached the table and proceeded to examine the contents of the covered dishes with a curiosity that was far from scientific.

The sight and smell of the main course, a crisply roasted chicken, was more than the good doctor could stand. Though he began with the idea of merely sampling, Stukeley did not stop until he had devoured the entire fowl. When finished, he carefully replaced the cover over the bones so as to make it seem that no one had trifled with the dinner of the master of the house.

Dr. Stukeley now resumed his waiting, smiling at the thought of what Newton would say on discovering that the best part of his meal was gone. In a little while the latter wandered up from the cellar.

He looked shocked and apologetic on seeing his caller. "I must have been in the cellar a long time," he said abstractedly. "I went there to get a bottle of wine—but I suddenly thought of something. And—and I left the wine there after all. I beg of you to forgive me, Dr. Stukeley." Newton appeared genuinely upset.

"Oh, it's nothing at all, nothing at all," Stukeley assured the embarrassed mathematician. "I didn't mind sitting here quietly, alone with my thoughts. In fact, I rather enjoyed the experience."

While they were talking about other matters, Newton went to the dinner table and absently lifted the cover of the main dish. He looked a little startled at seeing the heap of bare bones which the enterprising Stukeley had so thoughtfully left. After puzzling over this unnatural phenomenon for several seconds, Newton turned to his friend with great amusement.

"How absent-minded we philosophers are," observed the author of the *Principia*, as he hastened to drop the cover over the unappetizing remains of the roast chicken. "I thought I had not dined, but I see that I have."

In 1701, feeling secure in his Mint position, Newton resigned his professorship at Trinity. William Whiston, an able mathematician who had been acting as Newton's deputy in

Cambridge, was appointed to the Lucasian Chair largely on his predecessor's recommendation.

The University to which he had brought world-wide fame by his work in mathematics and science showed its appreciation by again sending Newton to Parliament. And two years later, in 1703, the Royal Society elected its most prominent member to the Presidency, a post to which he was annually re-elected until his death. And in 1705, Queen Anne conferred a knighthood upon the author of the *Principia*—an extraordinary distinction at that time, for Newton was the first English scientist to be so honored.

Everything was going well for Sir Isaac, and he felt happy and relaxed perhaps for the first time in his life. The sores caused by old controversies had healed, and the animosities which had plagued him for so many years were now mere memories. How Newton hated those petty conflicts with human beings! He had had his fill of accusations and counter-accusations, of suspicions and counter-suspicions.

It was fortunate that the reserved, peace-loving Sir Isaac enjoyed to the full these precious years of tranquillity. Little did he know that, after a ten-year period of quiet, a final academic storm would break around him! The celebrated—or perhaps notorious—controversy between the followers of Newton and those of Leibnitz over the credit for inventing the calculus is known to all students of mathematics. It was a disgraceful episode in which unscholarly violence was displayed on both sides by embittered partisans. Today most experts are of the opinion that Newton and Leibnitz each invented the calculus independently; and this was the expressed view of Newton himself before adherents of each side filled the air with suspicions.

But to get back to the peaceful years at the beginning of the century. . . . During this period Newton was often called upon to answer criticisms of various ideas in the *Principia.* Confident of the correctness of his principle, he was undisturbed by the opposition of scientists and philosophers to the views expressed in that massive work. Newton felt certain that time would prove the reliability of the mathematical outlook he had developed.

One idea that managed to stir up considerable discussion on the Continent had to do with the exact shape of the earth. Newton was of the opinion that, as a result of the rotation around its axis, the earth bulged slightly at the equator and was correspondingly flattened at the poles. The author of the *Principia* went so far as to apply his theory to the planet Venus. Newton asserted that if the exact extent of the flattening at the poles of that planet were known, it would be possible to compute the length of time it takes for Venus to make a complete rotation on its axis!

In France, a number of prominent scientists disagreed with Newton on the matter of the earth's shape. They were of the opinion that there was absolutely no flattening at the poles. Picard's famous measurements of the earth's dimensions, they pointed out, had failed to reveal any bulge at the equator or flattening at the poles.

In 1684 and again in 1701, a series of careful measurements were made in different parts of France. If Newton was right, the number of miles per degree of latitude should increase as one moves north. The investigating scientists found no evidence of any such variation.

Halley informed Newton of the negative results of the 1701 researches in France on the shape of the earth.

"Observations will have to be made nearer the poles before any increase in miles per degree of latitude will become apparent," the older man said confidently.

"They keep citing Picard's figures," noted Halley. "But

Picard himself pointed out that his work was carried on over too short a distance to prove anything conclusively about the shape of the earth."

"The differences in France, no matter whether measurements are made in the north or south, will be too minute . . . only a small fraction of a mile per degree. The present-day instruments are too crude to detect such small deviations," said Newton thoughtfully.

Halley nodded. "The French refuse to be convinced of the flattening. In fact, they are already considering still another measuring project."

Newton eyed his friend quizzically. "In France again?"

"Yes," said Halley.

Newton was silent for several seconds. "And what do they think is the true shape of the earth?"

"Well, they don't believe as you do that it's flattened at the poles. And at the same time they don't regard the earth as being a perfect sphere," answered Halley.

"Then what do they say it is?" persisted Newton.

Halley smiled and shook his head dubiously. "Many are convinced that the earth is elongated at the poles rather than flattened. They think it is more or less shaped like an egg."

"I don't think so," said Newton quickly. "I examined the arguments for that point of view and did not find them valid."

And so the disagreement over the shape of the earth persisted in scientific circles. In 1718, a set of measurements were made in France, and again no evidence of polar flattening was detected.

Years later, in 1735, the French Academy undertook to settle once and for all the troublesome question of the earth's exact shape. It was decided to send out two well-equipped expeditions—one to Lapland and the other to Peru. At these distances from the equator, an increase in the number of miles per degree of latitude should become noticeable—assuming that the Newtonians were right.

Sixteen months later, the Lapland group returned. Its leader announced that he had found without question that the earth was flattened at the poles.

Although the younger French scientists accepted the Lapland measurements as definitely settling the question in favor of Newton, the French Academy still hesitated to give up its egg-shaped earth. It was decided by the governing body of the latter organization that no conclusions be drawn until the southern expedition had reported its findings.

Finally, the Peru investigators got back to France with the information that they, too, had found conclusive evidence of flattening at the poles. The conservative element in the French Academy could hold back no longer. Shortly afterward it was officially accepted that Newton was right: the earth was not shaped like an egg!

Today, we know that the earth's diameter at the equator is nearly twenty-seven miles greater than it is at the poles.

20

FINAL DAYS

One misty spring morning in 1721, a nervous young man paused before a house in Martin Street, London, just off Leicester Square. It was an impressive, three-story stone structure to which Newton had moved some ten years before.

Henry Pemberton wondered at the reception he would receive from the great Sir Isaac. John Keill, a member of the Royal Society, had given the former a letter of introduction to England's noted scientist and mathematician. "Just be natural with him," Keill had advised. "Sir Isaac is a gracious scholar and never fails to respond to youthful enthusiasm and ability."

Ability? said Pemberton to himself ruefully. Who was he, Pemberton, but a mere youngster, still in his twenties, who had been accidentally attracted to mathematics through reading a borrowed copy of the *Principia*? It had happened while he was still a medical student at Leyden.

How would he explain to Newton what had brought him to Martin Street on this particular morning? Sir Isaac would laugh at the brash young doctor for offering to edit the third edition of the *Principia*!

"Roger Cotes was even younger than you when he edited

the second edition," Keill had assured him. "The world is waiting for someone to revise Cotes's edition and I think you are the man to do it. Newton is almost eighty years old now and realizes what an enormous task the editing and correcting will be. The job is made for you, Pemberton, I know it is!"

Henry Pemberton drew a deep breath and knocked on the door. In a few minutes he found himself in Sir Isaac's study. While Newton was reading Keill's letter, the young man studied the face of the most famous English scientist of all time.

Newton's shock of hair was now silver-white. He could still read without the aid of spectacles even at his advanced age. In spite of a lifetime of irregular hours of sleeping and eating, he appeared in excellent health. Pemberton noted with interest the wide brow, the long thin nose, the gentle demeaner of the illustrious mathematician.

The young visitor soon found himself talking freely without nervousness or embarrassment. He told of how the accidental reading of the *Principia* had fired him with the desire to learn more about the method of fluxions. It all seemed so involved, so difficult to understand at first; but as he steeped himself in mathematics, it all began to clear up, leaving him a captive to its beauty.

Newton nodded and smiled. "I understand that you wrote a paper answering the objections to the law of gravity put forth recently by a professor at Padua," he remarked.

"I did, Sir Isaac."

"Keill showed me your reply and I thought it revealed excellent mathematical skill," commented Newton. "Young men with a true love for science and mathematics are uncommon, and should be treasured when found—even though they may be students of medicine."

It was the beginning of an unusual friendship. Henry Pemberton, charmed by Newton's kindness and generosity, soon found himself busy editing the third edition of the *Principia*. He turned out to be a most fortunate choice. Newton, as in the case of Roger Cotes, had again selected the ideal person for a most difficult job.

"It is remarkable," the elated Pemberton said to Keill, "how different Newton is from what gossip had led me to expect. His mind is still flexible—even at eighty. And he isn't the least bit dogmatic. In spite of his position and accomplishments, his attitude toward the world remains humble. When I offer corrections, he accepts them with satisfaction—almost pleasure. What a wonderful man!"

Keill laughed and slapped the young man on the back. "As I once told you, there is nothing Newton will stop at to help a young mathematician. In the past, he has opened his purse to them, found teaching positions for gifted young men, even published their work at his own expense!"

The Scotsman was not exaggerating. Newton, after working with the brilliant Roger Cotes, would not rest until the latter had been installed as the first Plumian Professor of Mathematics at Cambridge—at the age of twenty-five! In the opinion of scholars, Cotes had done a magnificent job on the editing of the second edition of the *Principia*.

Colin Maclaurin, who later became Scotland's leading mathematician, was another brilliant young man whom Newton helped to get started. The latter used his influence to obtain a professorship at the University of Edinburgh for young Maclaurin; in fact, in his letter of recommendation, England's leading scientist even offered to pay twenty pounds a year toward the young man's salary!

Until he reached his eighty-first year, Newton's body had served him remarkably well. Except for that nervous breakdown which occurred after his superhuman exertions over his

Principia, he had seldom been ill during his entire life. For this reason, the sudden onset of a kidney ailment after so long a period of health shocked Newton and his friends.

"No moving around at all. Even the motion of a coach can be injurious," said Dr. Mead to Newton's niece, now Catherine Conduitt. She had married a few years before, but still lived in the Martin Street house with her husband John.

"What can I do to help him?" asked Catherine tremulously. The slim, dark-haired, keen-eyed young lady was overcome at the thought that her uncle, to whom she owed so much, was about to enter a period of pain and suffering.

"He is to eat little meat. Give him broth, fruit and vegetables. But the main part of the cure is rest, and there is to be no moving about at all."

Newton took his illness cheerfully, and arranged to have John Conduitt take over most of the duties at the Mint. Except for weekly visits to the Royal Society, the sick man obeyed his doctor's orders faithfully.

Since he was in pain only occasionally at first, Newton soon found ways of making his enforced rest both pleasant and productive. He spent considerable time on the old mathematical problem of the moon's motions; he worked with Pemberton on the revision of the *Principia;* and he occupied himself with the study he loved best—Biblical research.

With the inevitable weakening of his constitution due to advancing age, new ailments set in. In 1724, he suffered an attack of the gout, and soon afterward acquired a hacking cough caused by inflammation of the lungs. His doctors blamed the polluted air of London for the cough, insisting that the patient be removed to the village of Kensington, not far from the metropolis.

Newton objected to the change, but was finally persuaded. All his life he had disliked moving about; from Woolesthorpe to Cambridge to London was travel enough for him. Until late in life, he had steadily refused to make the short trip from London to Oxford! It seemed that Isaac Newton required a certain physical stability or fixedness for his work; the immobility of his body acted as a solid fulcrum for the lever which was his mind.

The change to Kensington appeared to do him good; for a short time, most of his pain disappeared. On recovering his clarity of mind, Newton turned to his Bible once again. He was now grappling with his last problem—the significance of life and death. To him, the life men know is but a minute part of an immense curve. Newton, like countless human beings before and after him, puzzled over the unrevealed part of the curve. What was its nature *before the beginning* and *after the end* of the earthly fragment?

In February, 1727, he insisted on going to London to preside as usual at the weekly meeting of the Royal Society. As a result of this exertion, he became violently ill. The sick man lingered on, in great pain, while his doctors stood by helplessly; during occasional intervals of relief, he would call for his books and concentrate on his favorite studies.

Isaac Newton passed away on March 20, 1727, in his eighty-fifth year, and was buried in Westminster Abbey several days later. His death was regarded as a national loss. All England paid honor to the memory of the genius among men who had done so much to enlarge human horizons, and who taught mankind how to discover new truths.

To the very end, Isaac Newton displayed a characteristic humility toward his own accomplishments. How he regarded himself and his life's work is beautifully expressed in his own memorable words:

"I do not know what I may appear to the world; but to

myself I seem to have been only like a boy playing on the seashore and diverting myself in now and then finding a smoother pebble or prettier shell than ordinary, whilst the great ocean of Truth lay all undiscovered before me."

BIBLIOGRAPHY

Dictionary of National Biography, vol. xiv, pp. 371-2, 393, Oxford University Press, London, 1921-1922.

Essays on the Life and Work of Newton, Augustus De Morgan, Open Court Publishing Co., Chicago, 1914.

Isaac Newton, Louis T. More, Charles Scribner's Sons, New York, 1934.

Isaac Newton, J.W.N. Sullivan, The Macmillan Co., New York, 1938.

Memoirs of Newton's Life, William Stukeley, M.D., Edited by A. Hastings White, Taylor and Francis, London, 1936.

Memoirs of the Life, Writings, and Discoveries of Sir Isaac Newton, Sir David Brewster, 2 volumes, Little, Brown, and Co., Boston, 1835.

Sir Isaac Newton, Selig Brodetsky, Methuen and Co. Ltd., London, 1927.

* * * *

Autobiography of Science, edited by F.R. Moulton and J.J. Schiffries, pp. 171-196, Doubleday, Doran and Co., New York, 1945.

A History of Science, Sir William Dampier, pp. 160-216, The Macmillan Co., New York, 1942.

Makers of Science, Ivor B. Hart, pp. 138-172, Oxford University Press, London, 1924.

Masterworks of Science, edited by J.W. Knedler, Jr., pp. 171-243, Doubleday and Co., New York, 1947.

Men, Mirrors, and Stars, G. Edward Pendray, Harper and Brothers, New York, 1946.

A Short Account of the History of Mathematics, W.W. Rouse Ball, Macmillan and Co. Ltd., London, 1901.

* * * *

History of England, Lord Macaulay, 2 volumes, Longmans, Green and Co., London, 1926.

Illustrated English Social History, G.M. Trevelyan, vol. 2. Longmans, Green and Co., London, 1951.

INDEX

INDEX

INDEX

About the Author

HARRY SOOTIN, a native New Yorker, received his B.S. from the College of the City of New York where he majored in chemistry. His first job was as an industrial chemist; then an appointment to teach in a New York City high school materialized, and he has been teaching for over twenty-five years. He turned to writing biography when he discovered that the human stories behind scientific discoveries always worked wonders in the classroom. Mr. Sootin has also written for magazines and for *Britannica Junior*. He makes Flushing, New York, his home.